YoungWriters 2005 PO

PLAYGROUND Poets

Let your creativity flow...

ode

limerick | haiku

rhyme

bal

Heart Of England

Edited by Steve Twelevetree

 Young**Writers**

First published in Great Britain in 2005 by:
Young Writers
Remus House
Coltsfoot Drive
Peterborough
PE2 9JX
Telephone: 01733 890066
Website: www.youngwriters.co.uk

SB ISBN 1 84602 170 7

Foreword

Young Writers was established in 1991 and has been passionately devoted to the promotion of reading and writing in children and young adults ever since. The quest continues today. Young Writers remains as committed to the fostering of burgeoning poetic and literary talent as ever.

This year's Young Writers competition has proven as vibrant and dynamic as ever and we are delighted to present a showcase of the best poetry from across the UK. Each poem has been carefully selected from a wealth of *Playground Poets* entries before ultimately being published in this, our thirteenth primary school poetry series.

Once again, we have been supremely impressed by the overall high quality of the entries we have received. The imagination, energy and creativity which has gone into each young writer's entry made choosing the best poems a challenging and often difficult but ultimately hugely rewarding task - the general high standard of the work submitted amply vindicating this opportunity to bring their poetry to a larger appreciative audience.

We sincerely hope you are pleased with our final selection and that you will enjoy *Playground Poets Heart Of England* for many years to come.

Contents

Ledbury Primary School, Ledbury

Elisha White (9)	54
Rebecca Pritchard (9)	55
Chloe Stokes (8)	55
Sara Nicklin (9)	56
Abi Rendle (10)	56
Edward Neale (9)	56
Hannah Jones (9)	57
Laura Bradley (9)	57

Mordiford CE Primary School, Mordiford

James Clough (9)	58
Bryony Rogers (10)	58
Evie Gullis (10)	58
Will Price (10)	59
Will Pritchard (10)	59
Tom Taylor (11)	60
Heidi Jackson (11)	60
Ashley Stanton (10)	61
Lucy Abbiss (11)	61
Alison Gardner (10)	62
Sarah Scotford (9)	62
Hannah Goulding (11)	63
Harry Abbiss (9)	63
Benjamin Turner (10)	64
Charlie Hodges (11)	64

Northleigh CE Primary School, Malvern

Julia Bijl (9)	65
Niamh Canning (7)	66
Morgan David Mason (7)	66
Lucy Constable (9)	67
Kali Williams (8)	67
Emma Dawson (7)	68
Fraser Savage (7)	68
Ross Mulka (8)	68
Katherine Stokes (10)	69
Rowan Hayes (10)	69
Skye Hope Gamble (9)	70
Cameron Heaton (8)	70
Isobel Mathias (10)	71
Luke Stanton (11)	71

Emma Knowles (10)	72
Sophie Cornelius (11)	73
Jared Maxfield (10)	73
Amie Bradshaw (10)	74
James Merley (10)	74
Eric Carlen (11)	74
Joe Whitehouse (8)	75
Kate Richards (9)	75
Frankie Shackleton (9)	75
Charlotte Jakeman (10)	76
Mia Alford (9)	76
Mary Fleming (11)	77
Zoë McKerr (8)	77
Laura Sockett (9)	78
Alexandra Garwood Walker (8)	78
Isabel Ellis (9)	79
Alexandra Smith (10)	79
Charlie Bytheway (10)	80
Kieran Jeffrey (10)	80
Jessica Smith (10)	81
Sophie Dawson (11)	81
Declan Amphlett (8)	82
Gemma James (9)	82
Amy Straughan (9)	83
Stuart Hawkins (9)	83
Jamie MacKenzie (9)	83
Catherine Fleming (9)	84
Heidi Loveridge (9)	84
Hannah Kenyon (10)	84
Zoë Burbeck (9)	85
Lucy Cooper (9)	85
Ben Jones (8)	86
Jake Stromqvist (9)	86
Rhys Alyn Griffiths (9)	86
Jordan Heudebourck-Rice (7)	87
Jeremy Bijl (9)	87
Ellie Cornelius (8)	87
Maxwell Bytheway (7)	88
Jacob Lambon (8)	88
Ruth Stromqvist (9)	88
Charlie Onions (8)	89
Rosie Milner (8)	89

Rebecca Lockton (9)	89
Chris Need (7)	90
Gary O'Callaghan (7)	90
Annabel Pearson (8)	90
Amara Devi (8)	91
Lucy Ellaway-Bell (8)	91
Harriet Walker (9)	91
Luke Maisey (8)	92
Ethan Bristow (9)	92
Noah Thompson (7)	92
Aaron Boden (7)	93
Laura Dixon (8)	93
Laurie Essenhigh (7)	93

Our Lady's Catholic Primary School, Alcester

Amy Campbell (10)	94
Kimberly Badoud (10)	94
Kristi Kelly (10)	94
Becky Cunningham (10)	95
Hannah Campbell (10)	95
Rachel Hendry (11)	96
Daniel O'Neill (9)	96
Sarah O'Reilly (10)	97
Samantha Preece (11)	97
Charlie Stanley (11)	98
Lucie Watson (11)	98
Shannon Hall (11)	99

Race Leys Junior School, Bedworth

Lani Duncan (8)	99
Ellen Smith (7)	100
Connor Keely (7)	100
Amy Cadman (11)	100
Jordan Randle (10)	101
Amy Hawthorne (8)	101
Luke Davis (10)	101
George Taylor (10)	102
Dale Walker (10)	102
Danny Kelly (10)	102
Josh Greenway (11)	103
Lewis Delich (10)	103

St Nicholas CE Middle School, Pinvin

Salford Priors Primary School, Salford Priors

The Willows CE Primary School, Stratford-upon-Avon

Rachael Finch (8)   182
Kane Hutchinson (9)   183

Witton Middle School, Droitwich
Jessica O'Hara (11)   183
Eleanor Gow (11)   184
Amelia Quiney (10)   185
Ceri Ann Jones (9)   185
Alexander Peirce (11)   186
Luke Pilot (11)   186
Dale Hawkes (11)   186
Harriet Hughes (11)   187
Jemma Mortimer (10)   187
Anwen John (11)   188
Alice Spearing-Brown (10)   188
Jess Goodall (10)   189
Andrew Bishop (11)   189
Abbi Cottrell (9)   190
Elizabeth Hotham (11)   190
Jasmine Davis (10)   191
Gabrielle Smith (10)   191
Jade Thompson (11)   192
Matthew Ramage (10)   192
Kyley Hallett (11)   193
Nathan Harold (11)   193
Saskia Cossum (10)   194
William Brockett (10)   194
Ashley Harris (10)   195
Michael Kirkham (10)   195
Lauren Whiteman (10)   196
Cerise Bartlett (11)   196
Alice Baren (9)   197
Charlotte Taylor (11)   197
William Chambers (10)   198
Harry Bourne (10)   198
Beth Killing (11)   199
Tyler-Rose Neath (10)   199
Tamsyn Webley (11)   199
Naomi Collins (11)   200

The Poems

Instruments

Dash! Bash! Crash!
Racing in the car,
With my expensive base guitar.
Singing in the microphone,
Wishing I was all alone.
Banging on the drums,
Sounding like shooting guns!
Playing on the tambourine,
Seeing yourself
On the big plasma screen.

Hannah Darbyshire (9)

An Orchestra Without A Conductor

An orchestra without a conductor,
Is like pizza without cheese.
An orchestra without a conductor,
Is like the trees without their leaves.

An orchestra without a conductor,
Is like a wizard without his staff.
An orchestra without a conductor,
Is like a teacher without her class.

An orchestra without a conductor,
Is like fire without smoke.
An orchestra without a conductor,
Is like a women without her bloke.

An orchestra without a conductor,
Is like football without the players.
An orchestra without a conductor,
Is like cake without its layers.

An orchestra without a conductor,
Is like short without long.
This is what I say,
'Oh where has that conductor gone?'

Ieuan Griffiths (10)
Abbey Park Middle School, Pershore

The Penguin

They slide across the ice so fast and drink
upon the water.
If you feel them, they are
Ice-cold, even colder!
If you ever see one, you will surely be dazzled.

They all like to play upon the shore, alone.
They cannot fly in the sky so high.
They really are a mess.

Swimming fast in the water,
About 80 miles an hour.
Catch them if you can!

They have huge flippers, enormous in fact,
So slowly they jaunt across the lands.

George Walker (8)
Brockhampton Primary School, Bringsty

The Ostrich Song

Big fluffy wings,
Long clawed feet,
The ostrich is so funny
It does not eat meat!

Flapping crazily,
It wants to fly,
It is very sad
But it cannot cry.

The babies are little
But little their eggs are not!
The eggs are massive, bigger than big
And babies, they don't half trot!

Fiona E Miles (9)
Brockhampton Primary School, Bringsty

The Robin

The robin sits on the snow
Waiting for the flowers to grow,
It lives in a woodland park
Where it is not attacked by a shark.

The robin is not such a clot
Even though it might live in a pot,
But it might get out, you never know,
It might even live in the snow.

Amy Hutchinson (8)
Brockhampton Primary School, Bringsty

The Golden Pheasant

The golden pheasant so, so pretty
Colours all around,
Hardly ever seen or never found.
Trying to fly, oh so high!
Like the other birds in the sky.

Beth Dennis (9)
Brockhampton Primary School, Bringsty

The Pheasant

I see a pheasant,
Oh that little peasant,
Eating all my corn,
Blow my signal horn.

I see a pheasant,
Looking very pleasant,
Now he has been fed,
He's off to find his bed.

Katherine Whistance (9)
Brockhampton Primary School, Bringsty

The Ostriches

They flap their wings,
Run so fast and swiftly,
They can't fly!

They are so tall
But when they're babies
They are so small.

Their feathers sway
In the wind.

Phillippa Rosie Bond (8)
Brockhampton Primary School, Bringsty

Blue Tit

Its yellow breast as bright as gold,
Flapping its blue beautiful wings.
Swaying in the breeze.
As it walks across the ground
Its blue little tail bobs up and down.
Catching worms as she feeds her chicks.

Henry Roper (9)
Brockhampton Primary School, Bringsty

Blue Tit

It's happily playing in the water,
Bright yellow covering its breast.
A dazzling white shields its head.
Flapping madly and playing with friends,
Look at its amazing ice-cold blue wings.

Christopher Maddock (9)
Brockhampton Primary School, Bringsty

The Golden Eagle

Golden eagles fly so high,
Across the mountains, in the sky,
Through the trees to its nest,
And finds food, its chicks rest.
The storm is coming, what a breeze
Find the shelter, full of leaves
Comfort, warmth.
The storm will go, the shelter will stay.
The chicks are resting amongst some hay.
The storm has gone for the day.

Conor Stobart (9)
Brockhampton Primary School, Bringsty

The Penguin

The penguin slides across the ice,
And falls into the sea.
It buries its eggs between its legs,
And makes them warm with glee.

A baby penguin is grey and fluffy,
And when it's born it's short and stubby.
A shame a penguin cannot fly,
But throughout its life it will try and try.

Flora May Lewis (9)
Brockhampton Primary School, Bringsty

The Red Kite

A fast bird that glides,
                so fast . . .
It hunts swiftly,
                so fast . . .
A scavenger,
                so fast . . .

Angus Walker (8)
Brockhampton Primary School, Bringsty

Pied Wagtail

I can see a pied wagtail
As soft as can be,
Suddenly he falls into a birdbath
And now he's watery!

His feathers are all scrubbed back
And now he starts to rap . . .
'P-i-e-d wagtail, wagtail, p-i-e-d wagtail.'

You can see his fluffy tummy,
Then he sees some plump round flies,
Yum-yum!

His feet are as black as night,
But still he doesn't give you a fright.

Emily Rooke (8)
Brockhampton Primary School, Bringsty

Blue Tits

Blue tits,
Singing high.
Fly, fly, fly
Flying high, over the sky.
Finding food, peanuts, nuts and caterpillars too.
Lives all year round, lives for you.
Fly, fly, fly
Spring, summer, autumn and winter too.
Blue tits green, yellow and white.
Flying to its nest to keep the chicks warm.
Fly, fly, fly.

Keely Thornton (9)
Brockhampton Primary School, Bringsty

The Chaffinch

The chaffinch sits between the trees,
Eating insects and his seeds.
Calling family and his friends,
To come and join him in his games.

Scampering about in the green bushes,
Trying to find somewhere to hide,
Under the coloured leaves.

His bright colours on his wings give
His hiding place away.
Now he has been found,
And they start another game.

Katie Price (8)
Brockhampton Primary School, Bringsty

Bald Eagle

Its head is as white as snow
Swooping by the sun
Gleaming in the sunlight
Stalking its prey.
Falling like a thunderbolt
Until it touches land.
It's caught prey
Going to its chicks.
Now it's time to feed them
And that's an eagle's life.

Jordan Whiteley (9)
Brockhampton Primary School, Bringsty

The Pheasant

The pheasants run in every field
Eating corn with a collared face.
The male and female scamper about,
Their brown and orange feathers glint in the sunlight.
Two male pheasants would start a fight
Over a piece of food in the day or night.
The baby pheasants walk around,
Following wherever she goes.

Georgie Clark (9)
Brockhampton Primary School, Bringsty

The Woodpecker

Woodpecker, woodpecker
What do you see?
Turn around and look at me.
Woodpecker, woodpecker
What do you see?
You see food up in the tree,
Woodpecker, woodpecker,
Fly away.

Fly, fly, fly away.

Jodie Loris (8)
Brockhampton Primary School, Bringsty

Darkness

Darkness is black, like the depth of the ocean
It sounds like the hooting of the owl
Eating its prey.
It looks like a spinning hole in space,
It smells like burning charcoal
It reminds me of a sharp rock
It feels like death.

Cameron Dunnett (7)
Cradley CE VA Primary School, Cradley

World War II, A Tank Driver's View

I can see . . .
Dead men lying around.
Soldiers with their guns blasting the Germans
Blown-up tanks flying in the air,
Aeroplanes crashing on the beach
Men jumping out of planes.
I can feel . . .
The ground beneath my feet shaking
The tank shaking,
The tank going backwards and firing at the Jerries
The Jerries, bombing us,
The tank control panel.
I can hear . . .
The guns firing at each other.
The bombs falling and going *bang!*
The men screaming as they fall to their deaths.
The tanks blowing up
Everyone screaming and shouting.
People shouting swear words
A woman screaming as her family dies.

Scott McNally (11)
Cradley CE VA Primary School, Cradley

Darkness

Darkness is the colour of black,
It is like the end of life.
It sounds like the stab of a knife in your throat,
It looks like prey being killed on the ground.
It smells like stinking rats down in the sewers.
It reminds me of death.
It feels like blood running down my body.

Michael Adair (8)
Cradley CE VA Primary School, Cradley

Hunger

Hunger is blue like your body going bone dry,
It looks like the sea, dead frozen.
It sounds like a volcano,
It tastes like your stomach eating itself.
It smells like bacon coming down your throat.
It reminds me of my worst nightmare,
It feels like rotten tomatoes squeezing your throat.

Josh Banner (8)
Cradley CE VA Primary School, Cradley

Hate

Hate is crimson like the Devil frying
Humans' guts on his barbecue of death.
It sounds like a never-ending nightmare.
It feels like a boxing match inside my heart.
It reminds me of a shadow creature
Stalking in the night.
It looks like a bursting volcano in the distance,
It smells like the burning of an oil ship,
It tastes like the squelching of someone's guts.

Christian Dandy (8)
Cradley CE VA Primary School, Cradley

Darkness

Darkness is black like the depths of the ocean,
Darkness sounds like the hooting of the owl, eating its prey.
Darkness looks like the swirling hole in outer space.
Darkness smells like the burning charcoal.
Darkness reminds me of death.
Darkness feels like shock and horror.

Bromlyn Cameron (8)
Cradley CE VA Primary School, Cradley

Love

Love is red like a heart,
It feels like a heart beating
It reminds me of a hamster
It tastes like blood.
It sounds like crying,
It looks like a rose.
Love is like people getting married.

Daisy Davies (8)
Cradley CE VA Primary School, Cradley

Anger

Anger is red like a devil in your dreams.
A volcano erupting,
A glass of jam.
The jam from a jam doughnut.
Cradley School jumpers.
The flames coming out of a dragon.
A nice rose.

Jai Smallwood (9)
Cradley CE VA Primary School, Cradley

Darkness

Darkness is black like the depths of the ocean,
It sounds like the hooting of the owl, eating its prey.
It looks like the swirling hole in outer space.
It smells like burning charcoal.
It reminds me of death,
It feels like horror and shock.

Amy Elizabeth Harte (7)
Cradley CE VA Primary School, Cradley

Henry VIII's Kingdom

What can you see?
A weeping woman in the corner.
A king in his rich clothes.
Henry throwing his gold in the air,
He has no respect.

What can you feel?
Blood dripping down my neck,
Henry counting his money,
Henry's clothes on Anne Boleyn's arms.
I can feel Henry's rich clothes.

What can you hear?
I can hear a weeping woman crying in the corner.
I can hear Henry laughing his head off.

Sophie A Davies (8)
Cradley CE VA Primary School, Cradley

My Bad Bathroom

What can you see?
A gooey toilet,
A slushy sink.
An out-of-date hard shampoo bottle
And the green and mouldy tiles.

What can you feel?
A wet and slimy toothbrush,
A rough and bumpy tap.
A half-empty glass of water,
And a wet and bumpy toilet flush.

What can you hear?
A tap running,
Steam coming out of the shower.
A Jacuzzi that doesn't work.
A jug of water spilling on the floor.

Zachary Kirkpatrick-Jones (9)
Cradley CE VA Primary School, Cradley

Anger

Anger is red like a bursting volcano,
It sounds like a thermometer exploding.
It looks like the Devil himself.
It tastes like red-hot chilli peppers,
It smells like blood, trickling down the knife.
It feels like all your blood running to your head.
It reminds me of what he has done.

Louis Boffy (7)
Cradley CE VA Primary School, Cradley

Fear

Fear is the colour of red, like burning flames,
It feels like hot fire
And it reminds me of a rocket launcher
But it smells like hot peppers
It tastes like white onions and
Looks like some blood juice
But it sounds like a nightmare.

Sam Walker (8)
Cradley CE VA Primary School, Cradley

Machines

M achines are loud
A lot of bangs
C aution signs everywhere
H orrifying machines
 I nvisible machines
N oble machines
E lectric machines everywhere
S uper strong machines.

Joshua Hodkin (9)
Cradley CE VA Primary School, Cradley

The Greed Of The Evil Dragons

'Mighty sword of wisdom protect me from this death.'
Yelled the mighty sword wizard as the giant dragon, Cerabrid,
Opened his mouth and let out a roaring ton of flame.

All around, the dragons were fighting, fighting for the lair.
The underground lair that the great Fang Ripper himself
Had taken over.

Now that he was dead, the dragons were fighting over
Who should own it and in all the confusion, the humans
Were about to *attack* . . . led by Sergeant Ciske, the wizard.

When the next rulers were killed by the other dragons,
The humans charged the courtyard. Cerabrid stopped breathing fire
At the sword wizard and turned around and flapped his great wings
Then rose into the air.

His great, long, wide, fat wings flapped constantly faster
So he rose higher, higher, higher and higher
And suddenly the sun was blotted out.
And then he dived down, down, down through the air.

And he turned up at the last moment and flew very low
And he opened his mouth and let out more flames
Than you could imagine and every soldier gasped and
Ran out of the courtyard. Then Sergeant Ciske swooped
Round the tower on his Sky-wings.

Noble Sky-wings opened his mouth and let out the best
Icy blast he had ever created.
The ice struck the dragon in the middle of the forehead and
knocked him down.
The ice spread over him like water over a pebble
Seeing this, all the other dragons flew and ran for it.

Sergeant Ciske yelled, 'The battle is won!
We can have our underground kingdom back from the dragons.'

Ciske Kroezen (9)
Cradley CE VA Primary School, Cradley

My Bathroom

What can you see?
Nine cats with nine lives swirling down the drain,
Wet ceilings looking like it was going to rain.
Mum running upstairs, needs the toilet in a rush,
One toilet that can't flush!

What can you feel?
Toilet water squirting on my face,
Trying to win a water-running race.
Water lying in the bath
No one knows about the secret path!

What can you hear?
The toilet flushing
The door creaking,
The breeze whistling
The bath running.

What can you taste?
The sickly taste in my mouth,
The nice breeze taste.
The gross taste of the toilet,
The taste of the bath water.

What can you smell?
The horrible smell of the toilet,
The shower water.
The toothpaste,
The horrible smell that toilets have!

P J Bennett (8)
Cradley CE VA Primary School, Cradley

I Have A Ferret

I have a ferret
Her name is Lucky
She's a funny little thing
And is always getting mucky.

I have a ferret
She wiggles her bum,
My bro thinks she's weird
But I think she's fun.

I have a ferret
She's the best pet of all
My mum doesn't like it when
She runs down the hall.

I have a ferret
Her name is Lucky
She's a funny little thing
And is always getting mucky.

Zoe Whatmore (10)
Cradley CE VA Primary School, Cradley

Vauxhall

V X220 speeds along
A stra's taking kids to school
U nderground tunnel filled with cars
X ara's Sintras sworn enemy
H igh up Vectras on a bridge
A 527 comes into view
L eather seats and air conditioning
L arge Zafira drives behind.

Jacob Scott (10)
Cradley CE VA Primary School, Cradley

Greece

Athens and Sparta were peaceful one year,
until it had a rear,
then Sparta had a thought,
and then they bought
an army which would fight for their land
like a crushing hand.

Then Darius wanted a place,
he returned in big disgrace,
and Athens, they celebrated,
then they just sat there and waited.
Then the Macedonians came to kill
they wanted to fight for free will.

The Romans came to Greece
Macedonia wanted peace, peace, peace.
Then war broke out
and the Romans had a big shout.
The Romans thought they had lots of luck,
and they moved across the sea like a rubber duck.

Finn Beesley (8)
Cradley CE VA Primary School, Cradley

Pancakes

Pancakes, you can flip them
They fly up in the air.
They whizz around the door
And splat on the floor.

Pancakes, pancakes, they're big or small,
They fly over the wall.
Yummy, they're good for your tummy.

Pancakes, eat them with your mate.
Man, they taste great!

Jamie Turner (9)
Cradley CE VA Primary School, Cradley

Water

I can see water coming down the mountain
Into the pools below.
I can see water plants.
I can see bubbles in the water where it hits the pool.

I can feel cool water,
Water plants brushing against me.
Gravel hitting me by the waterfall,
I can feel human's fishing lines.

I can hear the splashing of the waterfall,
I can hear the plonk of the human's rods.
I can hear other fish,
I can hear water plants swaying.

George Luke Banner (11)
Cradley CE VA Primary School, Cradley

World War II

I can see bombs booming all over,
I can see bullets zipping past.
I can see men dying in my sight,
I can see shouting and swearing on their lips.

I can feel the bumps in the tanks
I can feel bullets skimming my skin
I can feel all the tension on the battlefield
I can feel men pushing past me in the trench.

I can hear the screaming from dying men
I can hear a huge explosion in their trench
I can hear an engine of an English tank,
Thuds of footsteps behind me!

William Barnes (9)
Cradley CE VA Primary School, Cradley

Ancient Greek Warrior

What can you see?
I can see spurts of blood going everywhere,
People falling down dead,
Spears flying through the air,
Swords glistening in the midday sun.

What can you feel?
I can feel the handle of my sword,
The leather of the strap on my arm,
I can feel my blood-covered armour
And the sun beaming down on my face.

What can you hear?
I can hear swords clashing together,
The swords hitting the wooden shields.
The cries of people dying,
The squelch of mud under our feet.

Adam Johnson (10)
Cradley CE VA Primary School, Cradley

Pancake Day

P eople often eat me
A nd only one day a year
N ever eat me unless it's Shrove Tuesday.
C an you flip? Can you flop?
A nd then you burn me, cook me, eat me!
K ing, I'm king of the king's food I am, I am.
E at me now or I'll spit! Eat me.

D ropping lemon juice, sugar, golden syrup
A nd butter.
Y um-yum . . . bleugh . . . it's . . . it's . . . disgusting!

Angus Waters (8)
Cradley CE VA Primary School, Cradley

Pancake Day

P eople often eat them
A nd if it's Shrove Tuesday
N o one shouldn't eat one
C os it's the only day you get some
A nd you can put on sugar, butter, golden syrup and lemon juice
K ings and queens eat them
E verybody should

D elicious
A nd fresh from the fridge
Y um, yum, yum.

Freddy Van Vuren (8)
Cradley CE VA Primary School, Cradley

The Krull

The Krull is a dog barking in the night,
The Krull eats frogs from the garden.
The Krull lives on the street,
The Krull bites people's hands off
When he comes to seek.

The Krull makes people scream,
The Krull has teeth like a shark.
The Krull makes babies jump out of their prams.
The Krull is big, black and scary.

The Krull only comes out at night,
The Krull has white on it, like the snow.
The Krull makes noises at bedtime and goes . . .
'Hoooooowwwwwwwllll!'

Sally Booth (10)
Cradley CE VA Primary School, Cradley

The Front Line

I see my friends going before me,
Seeing the fate that lies ahead of me.
The smell of dead corpses captures my nose,
The route of the front line is what I chose.

I feel my heart burning inside of me,
As I remember my wife and two children,
I must get home to them,
I swore to them I'd return.

I hear the colonels cry of 'Go! Go! Go!'
I sprint and dive down low.
I take a shot at the enemy,
I know I have lied to my family
As I feel a bullet rip through my love-filled heart.

Tom Sparks (11)
Cradley CE VA Primary School, Cradley

The Moon

The moon sparkles . . .
Like a diamond in the sky.
Polished . . .
Like a round table in a dark room.
Glitters . . .
Like the world.
Twinkles . . .
Like a round shiny cup.
Beams . . .
Like a round space saucer.
Shines . . .
Around our planet all alone.

Jason Tipping (11)
Cradley CE VA Primary School, Cradley

Urban Terror

The cold night approaches
A scream of terror is unleashed,
Many twisters spill,
All terrorising the city
Sending it into chaos.
The gangs creep through uncharted alleys,
Snatching victims who are alone.
The population drops by fifty.
Its remainders are hiding under beds
Hoping not to be spotted.
At the heart of the storm and in the night,
The people on outings fall,
They cannot bear the terror,
Unleashed by a policeman's descent
Into nothing.

Mark Adair (11)
Cradley CE VA Primary School, Cradley

In My Bedroom

My big bed that's rattling in the corner,
My book on the shelf, waiting to be read.
The smell of the refreshing lavender
Sinking into my clothes.
The taste of the air whistling in my mouth,
The silky warm cover on my bed,
And the smooth, peaceful music.

Samuel Sparks (9)
Cradley CE VA Primary School, Cradley

Bullying

I feel upset, tears are dripping from my eyes,
Not a blink from the bully
But just a coward's look.

I am feeling scared, feeling weak
Standing there in the corner
No way out!

I try to run but I can't
The bully's like the red light on a traffic signal.
I see a friend but he can't hear me.
The bully kicks
Ouch! That hurts!

Feeling stupid, not the bully,
But me.

Callum Green (9)
Ledbury Primary School, Ledbury

Bullied

I feel stupid!
This morning my brother pushed me down the stairs.
I feel helpless!
Someone tripped me up at school.
I feel upset!
Someone threw my library book and ripped it.
I feel scared!
My sister pinned me down and took my pocket money.
I feel threatened!
My brother punched me.
I feel terrified!
I don't want to go out anymore!

Emily Earp (8)
Ledbury Primary School, Ledbury

Millie Molly Mandy

Millie Molly Mandy sat in some candy and
was well and truly stuck.
She cried and she cried and she cried even more
until she flooded the floor.
Her mum came downstairs and started to glare
at the terrible, terrible flood.
She smacked Millie Molly Mandy ever so hard
that she started to cry again and again.
So she started to cry again.

Jessica Simpson (9)
Ledbury Primary School, Ledbury

Easter - Haikus

Chicks are hatching now
Children are all excited
Shiny Easter eggs.

Yummy Easter eggs
Are falling in the sunshine
On Easter Sunday.

Kasihta Machae (9)
Ledbury Primary School, Ledbury

Bullies!

B ruises on the outside and also on the in,
U nderstanding how much it hurts.
L earning to control your temper,
L isten to me!
I 'm the one you're hurting,
E nemies we may be
S till there's no need to bully!

Danielle Griffin (10)
Ledbury Primary School, Ledbury

Being Bullied

I feel upset and weak,
someone tripped me up and I fell over
and banged my head,
and had to stay in my bed.

I feel threatened and bad inside
when I get picked on
I don't feel strong.

I feel furious and scared,
the bully always puts spiders
down my back and takes my hat,
and always gets a bumblebee.
Please don't keep on being horrible to me.

Jade Adams (9)
Ledbury Primary School, Ledbury

Being Scared

I feel scared, I feel bewildered,
I feel weak, I feel dread,
I feel furious, I feel bad,
I feel terrified and can't tell my dad.
I feel stupid, I feel sick inside,
I feel trapped and I want to hide.
I feel threatened, I feel down,
I feel like the bully is winning the gold crown.
I feel petrified, I feel bad about myself,
I feel like I'm losing my health.
I feel like I'm not taking it,
I feel like I'm going to lose it all.

Ethan Wood (8)
Ledbury Primary School, Ledbury

The Place

I lie on the sand
In perfect peacefulness
I dream about *now*.

The velvet softness
Of colourful, calm flowers
I dream about *them*.

The tropical fish
Swim below, a smooth blanket
I dream about *there*.

Soft, white clouds, like fur . . .
Cushioning the entire sky.
I dream about *that*.

I turn, look about
And I see every corner
As a perfect dream.

Ruth Nicoll (11)
Ledbury Primary School, Ledbury

Gerfunkness

I am a rainbow shadow,
That sucks your fears away,
I am the passionate dream you long for,
I am all the love you desire,
Gerfunkness, gerfunkness,
I am your happiness,
You should thank me,
The rainbow shadow you've never seen,
The love of your life!

Gemma Bullock (11)
Ledbury Primary School, Ledbury

Horse Riding

On Saturday morning
I get up and go horse riding.
Clippity-clop, clippity-clop,
Go the hooves.
I see the horse having fun,
Cantering around the field,
I go with my friend,
Danielle Howells.
We stick together all day long,
I ride on Ligall,
And have a giggle.
We do some jumps
After lunch.
We do have to pay
But . . .
We have a good day.

Alice Topham (10)
Ledbury Primary School, Ledbury

The Moon

The moon is a beautiful
Floating disc sailing
Through the sky.
You can see it clearly
When there are no clouds.
The moon is like a person
In outer space,
It is shiny, yellow and
Silvery white,
And travels round the Earth!

Claudia Locke (9)
Ledbury Primary School, Ledbury

The Man Who Lives Down Woodleigh Road

(Inspired by 'The Writer of this Poem' by Roger McGough)

The man who lives down Woodleigh Road
Is as tall as a tree
As keen as the north wind
As noisy as can be
As fast as a cheetah.

The man who lives down Woodleigh Road
Is as brave as a knight
As bold as a boxing glove
And now he's going to book a flight
Here he is above the night.

The man who lives down Woodleigh Road
Is as strong as a pole
As sharp as a nib
As small as a mole
As tricky as a fib.

The man who lives down Woodleigh Road
Never ceases to amaze
He's one in a million billion
(Or so the poem says!)

Joshua Williams (8)
Ledbury Primary School, Ledbury

Unicorns

A graceful white horse
Flying through the sky,
Wings as light as feathers.
A lovely sight to see so high.

A long golden horn
On the front of its head,
A pretty swirly horn
As delicate as silk thread.

Sophie Cockett (8)
Ledbury Primary School, Ledbury

Gold

The sun moves in his golden shoes,
The light of the sun peers upon us
In the blue sky.
The sun's golden coat warms the Earth,
The sun has a golden heart and golden eyes
Which beam its light across the sky.

The sun takes over Earth with its powerful light,
The sun, far away, lets the Earth warm
Before the moon takes over.

The sun warms us down here on Earth,
The sun does no harm and doesn't hurt,
All it does is beam on Earth.
The sun's powerful light helps
Warm the Earth and all living things.

Adam Dalley (8)
Ledbury Primary School, Ledbury

The Eye

When I look through the shining window
All I can see is a tearful eye.
This eye tells me about sadness,
Sadness in itself.
This eye is full of water,
Like a stream of jumping fish.
But this eye is like the fish,
Trying to swim against the currents.
It is trying to fight the tears,
As the fish fight the currents.
Maybe even like a person holding on for their life,
It can't hold on any longer.
The eye bursts into a tear and tears.

Jade Gibson (10)
Ledbury Primary School, Ledbury

Weather

I like sunny weather
playing outside
running around,
fun, fun, fun.

Rainy weather, it's okay
stuck indoors
doing nothing,
bore, bore, bore.

I like snowy weather
white everywhere
making snowmen,
brr, brr, brr.

Windy weather, it's okay
leaves doing a dance
getting pushed over,
ouch, ouch, ouch.

I like all kinds of weather
from rain to sun.
'But mummy, why oh why
can't it just stay the same?'

Alex Jones (11)
Ledbury Primary School, Ledbury

Being Bullied

I feel really weak
Now I want to cry,
I want to hit them back
But I feel smaller than a fly.

Now I feel threatened,
Now I'm running away.
Now I'm really scared
I know they're going to get me
At the end of the day!

Tyler Broughton (9)
Ledbury Primary School, Ledbury

Ancient Combat

Battle cries, arrow flies,
Shield wall stands up tall.
Battle horns roar, ravens soar,
Every single sword draws.

Leaders march, arrows arch,
Orders 'fire', the battle is dire.
Swords slash, shields crash,
Catapults sling, blasting the walls.

Women cry as their men die,
The battle stalls as darkness falls.
The breached wall is about to fall,
Into the enemy's hands.

The ravens come, the battles are won,
The armies retreat, they taste defeat,
For the winner's victory is sweet,
The enemy armies have been beat.

David Hassan Benhenni (11)
Ledbury Primary School, Ledbury

School Is Great

School is great
But you must tell
If things aren't going very well.
Whether it's punching or being unfair
You know the teachers really care.
If this is happening to you or me
Stand up tall
And say, quite clear -
'The bullies must stop
For our school to be top.'

Jessica Bevan (8)
Ledbury Primary School, Ledbury

Where Am I?

I wake up in the morning
when the sun has just come out
I sit up. Red, yellow and orange flames on my face
I stare over the dunes and ask myself -
Where am I?

I swim in the ocean
with all the tropical fish.
I stare into the glistening waters
and wonder -
Where am I?

I wander down to the shore
palm trees swaying in the breeze
I spot something on the horizon
a ship coming closer to me
as I wonder -
Where am I?

I watch the ship carefully
Until it is almost upon me
People disembarking scream
'Seize the island!'
I know where I am now.

Catherine Okey (10)
Ledbury Primary School, Ledbury

Young Martian

There was a young Martian from Mars,
Who ate too many chocolate bars,
He grew to be fat,
Like Garfield the cat,
That huge, young Martian from Mars.

Jordan Leigh Parry (11)
Ledbury Primary School, Ledbury

The Moon

The evening cools
The night-light darkens.
The moon rises like a ghostly face at night.
The many stars light up the sky
Like a million crystals.
The moon floats through the dark sky,
Like a silver ball, the moon is at its highest,
As darkness fills the background.
Everyone is resting,
As the time ticks away,
Dawn is breaking,
The moon is falling
Falling through the sky
Like a giant snowball
In the starlit sky.

William Blackaby (9)
Ledbury Primary School, Ledbury

A Rolling Stone

Will I die?
Is it the end?
Will all my bones
Break and bend?
How big is it?
Will I turn flat?
A huge pancake
Will I look like that?
Wait a sec -
Am I thick?
They just released an album
Called '40 Licks'!

Henry Cosh (10)
Ledbury Primary School, Ledbury

Fear And Relief

A loud howling
A low murmuring
Fear being pumped
Around my veins
A cold and sticky sweat
That freezes me so I cannot move
What is going on?
What shall I do?

A loud howling
A low murmuring
Scared as I am
I go to explore
I creep down the stairs
And pause as I touch
The red-hot door
Slowly and quietly
I open it.

I see Mum and Dad
Big grins on their faces
I see what they're looking at
'It's called Jasper,'
Whispers Mum.
I see the cute little puppy
Which belongs to me.

Abigail Philippa Smith (11)
Ledbury Primary School, Ledbury

Chesgophant

Chesgophant, chesgophant,
A blowing flower,
Or a magical power?
As nobody knows what it is.

Some people believe it sounds like
A violet violin,
A rose hip clarinet,
Or a golden daffodil trumpet.

Chesgophant, chesgophant,
Find the chesgophant,
Take a boat to the clouds
To find the chesgophant.

It's near a crumbling castle
Where ghosts still haunt,
And where giants roam the lands,
And where pots of gold are at ends of rainbows.

When you find the chesgophant
You shall have what your heart desires,
And all your wishes will come true,
Find the chesgophant, chesgophant, chesgophant.

Chesgophant, chesgophant,
A blowing flower,
Or a magical power?
As nobody knows what it is.

Beth Stinchcombe (11)
Ledbury Primary School, Ledbury

Cats

Long curly whiskers
A tail, long over its back.
Miaow, miaow, it does cry,
An animal extremely sly.
Black cats are lucky,
Playing in fields, really mucky.
Cats eyes nicely bright,
Seeing through the night.

Cats are pets,
Cats are wild.
Sneaking up on its prey,
Many cats are here to stay.
Big cats, small cats,
All eating nasty rats.
Long hair, short hair,
Try and catch one if you dare.

Cats I think, wish
For big juicy fish.
Some cats have small ears,
Many cats have no fears.
Fat cats, thin cats,
Sprawling across the mats.
These are my facts
About cats.

Laura Underhill (9)
Ledbury Primary School, Ledbury

Playing Mob

When you were counting I didn't know where to hide,
I was going to get caught . . . I knew it,
Until I found a very good hiding place,
Under a car.

I was trying to save my breath to run like a cheetah,
But I was still petrified, I wouldn't save all,
My friend would be 'it' and that's not right.

When you went up the street to find everyone all I heard was,
'Mob 1, 2, 3,' and, 'Come on Amy, you have to save all.'
You searched up and down, high and low and *still* couldn't find me,
You looked up the street once more, knowing you would catch me.

'This is my chance,' I said to myself.
'Go! Run like the wind,' I shouted, touching the tree.
'Mob 1, 2, 3, save!'
Everyone cheered except you,
I saved all, it was like saving the world.

Amy Walker (11)
Leominster Junior School, Leominster

My Rabbit Ernie

The day I got you
I was scared to death
I didn't know what to do
To stroke or to scream
But eventually I decided you were really cute
With your floppy ears
And your wriggly nose
And fluffy tail
I'd stroke you every day
For you're the best pal I've ever had
My pet rabbit Ernie.

Kirsty Millward (10)
Leominster Junior School, Leominster

My Magic Box

(Based on 'Magic Box' by Kit Wright)

I will put in my box . . .
The blue sky of a tropical country
The snow of the Himalayas
And an exploding volcano in Hawaii.

I will put in my box . . .
Three Siamese cats
Laughing at the ugly duckling
Butterflies from the green rainforest
The great Komodo dragon
Scattered over the Indian islands.

I will put in my box . . .
The blaze of the sunrise in the frosty morning
The moo of a healthy cow
The eye of a golden eagle.

I will put in my box . . .
Rocks from ancient Stonehenge
Fruits from the forbidden jungle
And a flying squirrel.

My box is fashioned from crystal and amethyst fossils
With a Mediterranean lid
And caves in the corners
Its hinges are from the old cupboard door
I shall dance in my box
On the great hills of the Scottish Highlands
Then twirl into the crystal waterfall - like the stars.

Jack Hedley (11)
Leominster Junior School, Leominster

My Magic Box

(Based on 'Magic Box' by Kit Wright)

I will put in my box . . .
The boy of my dreams in the Bahamas,
My memories of my nan,
And my best friend Amy.

I will put in my box . . .
My school friends,
My street,
Also something sweet to eat.

I will put in my box . . .
The best liked food,
A newborn baby,
And my photos of happy days.

I won't put in my box . . .
War against other countries,
Captured people,
Tortured animals,
Cos they're bad things and bad memories.

But I will put in my box . . .
People's freedom,
And me!

My box is made of a beech tree,
With silver-coated sides
That shines in the moonlight
And catches the starlight glitter.

Jasmine Harvey (10)
Leominster Junior School, Leominster

Going To Gwytherin

I'm moving to Wales in July,
I'm quite excited but I still cry,
It's in Gwytherin
On the edge of Snowdonia Park.
I feel quite sad,
For it's two hours away,
But I know inside I really want to go,
Because it's amazing there, it really is,
With its rivers and walks,
I'll never be bored again.
It's ever so quiet,
With no cars at all,
The pub is great,
Except for the kitchen,
It smells like a dead person's tomb!
The cottage is totally different,
As empty as plain paper,
With a fireplace in the front room,
And that is really it,
Every emotion I've ever had,
Are all mixed into one,
For I'm moving to Gwytherin,
With my sister, Dad and Mum.

Hebe Richardson (10)
Leominster Junior School, Leominster

The Magic Box

(Based on 'Magic Box' by Kit Wright)

I will put in the box . . .
One kitten with the sun's smile
A television with the clearest screen
And my teddy with a black and white tail.

I will put in the box . . .
A blanket with the warmth of fire
A pillow as soft as fur
And enough food to feed an army.

I will put in the box . . .
Hidden gold from a pirate's cave
A skateboard with wheels as fast as wind
And a jacket as warm as a bear's coat.

My box is bronze with silver coins
Twinkling stars reflect off the sides
The box can hold as many pebbles as a pebbly beach.

I shall run with my box
Along the great hills of the noisy forests
Then lie down beside the longest river
The colour of the pure sky.

Carla Biddle (11)
Leominster Junior School, Leominster

My Magic Box

(Based on 'Magic Box' by Kit Wright)

I will put in my box . . .
The sting of an angry swarm of wasps,
A red sunset before a full moon,
And a toenail of a raging lion.

I will put in my box . . .
The nicest bar of chocolate this land has ever seen,
A swimming pool with diving board,
And a blue sea with a golden beach.

I will put in my box . . .
A telly with every channel,
A 200mph Ferrari with a DVD player,
And a boat with a restaurant.

I will put in my box . . .
A season ticket for the best football team,
A whole set of golf clubs,
And a tennis court with a fence.

My box is fashioned from the first snow of the year,
A memory of your favourite grandad,
And a bark of an excited puppy.

I shall run in my box on a great athletic track,
Then race to the finish to collect my gold medal.

Jack Castle (11)
Leominster Junior School, Leominster

The Magic Box

(Based on 'Magic Box' by Kit Wright)

I will put in the box . . .
The love of a couple's first kiss,
A slight breeze in my hair,
The sound of water flowing in a river.

I will put in the box . . .
Microbes munching on a cell,
A black hole performing spaghettification,
And the glow of an eclipse.

I will put in the box . . .
An island in da sun,
The flashing lights of viva Las Vegas,
And the clatter of a metal rail.

My box is fashioned with metal, wood and rubber,
With decks on the lid,
And trucks in the corners.

I shall skate in my box,
On the grand high quarter pipes of skate mania,
I shall transfer and land,
Grinding on the gates of Heaven.

Zachary Bufton (10)
Leominster Junior School, Leominster

Majorca

The pool sparkled like the sea
It made me feel quite happy
The weather was hot
But the water was not
And that filled me with much glee

The beach had golden sand
So deep I could bury my hand
Well actually my body too
Perhaps even all of you
My feet burnt on the sandy land

You took me to different places
Brought more things to pack in suitcases
They got full to the top
Like they were going to pop
We must have Spanish crazes

Our room was on the top floor
And I thought, *cor!*
This really is quite high
Up in the bright blue sky
I could see the seashore.

Stephanie Ryan (10)
Leominster Junior School, Leominster

My Magic Box

(Based on 'Magic Box' by Kit Wright)

I will put in the box . . .
A supernova explosion from the depths of space,
The birth of a new star,
And the first signs of life on a faraway planet.

I will put in the box . . .
A caveman's beard swaying in the breeze,
A pre-historic painting,
And a woolly mammoth's tusks.

I will put in the box . . .
A flying unicorn with a white mane,
A phoenix feather,
And a golden wing of a gryffin.

I will put in the box . . .
A dark wizard and an evil witch,
The hiss of a poisonous snake,
And the slime from a slithering snail.

My box is created from the feathers of a golden eagle,
With the sun on the lid and adventures in the corners,
Its hinges are the spines of good books.

I shall fly in my box . . .
Above the fluffy white clouds,
And the dark grey storms,
Then swoop down and come to rest on an ancient oak tree.

Emlyn Rhys Washbrook (10)
Leominster Junior School, Leominster

Waiting

I have been waiting,
And waiting,
For nine months now.
Waiting in excitement,
Waiting in boredom,
Waiting for my life to change.
Please, please
Stop playing with my mind,
Like a cat playing with a mouse,
Stop keeping me in suspense.
Please Mum,
Please just have the baby.

Bethannie Cooper (11)
Leominster Junior School, Leominster

My First Hamster

I am waiting
For my little furry friend,
Excited,
I really want one,
They're cute,
It's my birthday soon,
Wow!
I dream every night,
It's black and white,
With patches,
A baby hamster
Who sleeps in my room
And *smells.*

Kiesha Hill (11)
Leominster Junior School, Leominster

My Magic Box

(Based on 'Magic Box' by Kit Wright)

I will put in my box . . .
An oriental dragon
With a tamer,
A rocketship to go to the moon.

I will put in my box . . .
A festival for me,
And world peace,
A Bonfire Night to remember.

My box is fashioned
With dragon scales,
Moonstones and
Oriental fabric.

My box will take me to strange lands
That nobody else has found
Over snowcapped mountains
Fiery deserts and the seven seas.

Danni Atkinson (11)
Leominster Junior School, Leominster

World War II

War was so bad
but we were glad.
The Blitz was horrid
everyone was worried.
All of the trenches
had terrible stenches.
There'll be scary frights
because they show no lights.
There's lots of gore
about the war.

Samantha Matravers (10)
Lindridge CE Primary School, Lindridge

Survivor In The Sky

Above the clouds in a time of danger,
Killing opponents beyond my reach,
Shooting and firing to save my country,
Fighting to create peace.
Scarred for life, destroyed by my fears,
Pushing buttons, searching for targets aiming to end this war -
Bullets hurtling in all directions,
Staring death straight in the eye.
Travelling to the safest place in the world,
Distraught and relieved
That I was alive to tell the tale.

Lottie Silver (11)
Lindridge CE Primary School, Lindridge

The Evacuee

'All aboard,' shouted the conductor.
The station master blew his whistle,
Then, with a sudden jolt, off the train went,
I wish in a way I hadn't been sent.
Through dark, dark tunnels,
Over rusty tracks we went on.
Then at last we stopped,
I was so tired I could have dropped.

I was taken to a small school,
Waiting for someone to pick me up.
Suddenly the door opened just a trace,
To reveal a lady's kindly face.
She took me on a horse and cart,
And over the hill to a lovely farm.
I'd never touched the horn of a bull,
Or the soft, warm feel of a sheep's white wool,
All I wanted was this war to finish,
And peace on Earth from end to end.

Alice Williams (9)
Lindridge CE Primary School, Lindridge

The Hungry Dragon

One cold night,
A dragon stomped through a lonely city,
Eating everything in its path.
He burned wandering people and ate them.
He was so big he crushed houses like we crush ants,
He crushed them to make them bite-sized.
He wandered through towering shopping malls eating all the food
and girls,
Then he smashed out through the doors to do the same
to another city.

Sam Andrews (8)
Lindridge CE Primary School, Lindridge

At Playtime!

I love to hang out
And sometimes to shout,
At playtime, at playtime.

My mates are so cool
And sometimes drive me up the wall,
At playtime, at playtime.

I love to do impressions
And ask lots of questions,
At playtime, at playtime.

I am really cool
But sometimes a fool,
At playtime, at playtime.

Eliza Thompson (10)
Lindridge CE Primary School, Lindridge

The Trench

It is horrible in a trench,
Because of the rats and the mighty stench.
But when you get used to the smell,
There isn't much to tell.

The Germans are the worst,
Always attacking first.
And when we do attack,
We're always running back.

James Lloyd (11)
Lindridge CE Primary School, Lindridge

My Dad's A Farmer

My dad is a farmer,
He works hard all day,
He feeds the cattle
With silage and hay.

He ploughs the fields
And drills the corn,
At springtime he's really busy,
Because new lambs are born.

Jonathan Bradley (11)
Lindridge CE Primary School, Lindridge

Fairies

When you see the fairies in your dreams flying through the air,
You wish you could be one of them, you wish you could be there.
Even though it's just a wish, it still could come true,
But before you believe in fairies, you must believe in you.

It's time for you to go now, time to go to bed,
But there is still one little thing that really must be said,
If you believe in fairies, then they'll believe in you,
That's the most important thing, may all your dreams come true.

Megan White (10)
Lord Scudamore Primary School, Hereford

Seasons

(Based on 'The Months' by Sara Coleridge)

January brings the snow,
Makes our feet and fingers glow.
February brings the rain,
Melts the frozen pond again.
March brings wind with a nasty bite,
To rattle doors in the night.
April has both sun and showers,
To wet your feet and grow the flowers.
May is the month of new green leaves,
When birds are nesting under eaves.
June contains the longest day,
With hours of sun for all your play.
Although July is very warm,
It also brings a thunderstorm.
August is full of hot, dry days,
Sea and sand and holidays.
September brings a cooler breeze,
Fruit and nuts upon the trees.
October turns the leaves to brown,
And chilly winds to blow them down.
Dull November dark and nippy,
Making roads and pavements slippy.
Cold December brings the sleet
And presents for your Christmas treat.

Vicky Day (11)
Lord Scudamore Primary School, Hereford

DT

DT is great
I like it more than a plate
You make things
You slate things
You really, really take things.

You make a little dolly
That looks like Miss Polly
You make little books
The ones that you took.

You bake things
You take things
The one that you like
You ride a little bike!

Leah Paige Chester (8)
Lord Scudamore Primary School, Hereford

Dear Nan

Dear Nan, dear Nan, I love you
And the clock that goes cuckoo.

You used to love to go to town,
With smiles for all, and not a frown.

I'll always have you in my heart,
Now I'm sad, because we're apart.

I miss the bird with the pecking beak;
He's gone away, now you're asleep.

I'll love you each and every day
And I'll think of you whilst I pray.

Aarron Ewart (9)
Lord Scudamore Primary School, Hereford

Cats

Cats are cuddly, cute and sweet
Even though they always sleep.
When they snuggle up to you
Because they're soft and cuddly.

Cats can get into mischief though
By breaking stuff and scratching stuff
But they were always meant to be tough.

When you leave water in the sink
And get something you might want to rethink that,
Because there might be someone
Having a drink in there!

But don't be mean to them
Just feed them and play with them
That's all you need to do.

Chloe Hannaford (10)
Lord Scudamore Primary School, Hereford

The Jungle

Take me down to the jungle city
Where the grass is green
And the flowers are pretty,
The river washing in a dream
The zebra nearby trying to clean
Wolves howl with bloodthirsty roar
A giraffe rips off a whole apple core
Monkeys swing, birds sing
Kangaroos bounce, tigers pounce
And that's the end of the day in the jungle
I feel hungry, I need apple crumble!

Josh Keane (10)
Martley Primary School, Martley

The Jungle

It's very hot and I am wet.
It's a bright day, there is a river in sight.
The river is calm and gentle as can be.
The birds are singing in the trees
And the leaves are all hot and sticky.
Then I hear a monkey swinging through the trees
He is as hairy as can be
And he has clammy fingers.

Sophie Tustin (10)
Martley Primary School, Martley

The Jungle

It is very hot and very sticky
The river is flowing very fast
A lion roars, it almost sings
Monkeys swinging through the trees
Screeching loudly, banging their chests
Slithering snakes everywhere
I would love to see Tarzan
He is the best.

Harry Taylor (9)
Martley Primary School, Martley

Jungle Life

In the jungle where the wild flowers grow
There's now people that you would know,
There is a slithering snake, *big* mistake,
Even a deer that can hear a little tear
Dropping from a crocodile's eye
A kangaroo jumping
An elephant bumping
That is jungle life!

Elisha White (9)
Martley Primary School, Martley

My Jungle Poem

I walked into the jungle
And what did I see?
A big, fat, hairy chimpanzee,
Up a tall tree.

Further on in the jungle I saw . . .
Four young lions biting their claws.

Look there's a snake,
Slithering to the lake.

All the animals
Happy as can be,
Open the door
And what do you see?
Animals!

Rebecca Pritchard (9)
Martley Primary School, Martley

In The Jungle

In the jungle where the palm trees grow I saw . . .
A tiger pouncing
A horse trotting
A snake slithering
A rabbit hopping
A lion roaring
An elephant stamping
A hyena laughing
A panther bouncing.
What did you see in the jungle?

Chloe Stokes (8)
Martley Primary School, Martley

The Jungle

In the African jungle
There are lions and tigers
Very busy birds sing
Swinging monkeys
Slithering snakes
Fallen trees and flying parrots
Tarzan swings
The sun is scorching
George of the jungle is having a rest
I can see his hairy chest!

Sara Nicklin (9)
Martley Primary School, Martley

In The Jungle

Down in the jungle where nobody goes
There's a big, hairy elephant having a doze
The flamingos are washing their toes
A panda is playing games whilst waiting in the shade.
A lion eats leaves and monkeys swing on trees.
Tigers roar and I can hear a snore.

Abi Rendle (10)
Martley Primary School, Martley

The Jungle

I am in the jungle and guess what I see?
A big, fat, hairy chimpanzee.
It ran off down to the river.
Then I saw a tiger eating someone's liver.
I moved on and saw a monkey swinging from a tree.
You could see its hair as plain as could be.
Now I am done in the jungle
That's all the animals in a bundle!

Edward Neale (9)
Martley Primary School, Martley

Down In The Jungle

Lions growl
Hounds howl

Parrots are pretty
So are wild kitties

Snakes go round trees
While monkeys go, 'Hee-hee!'

Dinosaurs roar
While the green grass stands tall

Monkeys have leaves
But I have sleeves

Sleep, sleep animals go
Tomorrow we will go, go, go.

Hannah Jones (9)
Martley Primary School, Martley

In The Jungle

Tigers growl
Wolves howl
Lions pounce
Koalas bounce
Tarzan swings
Monkeys fling
Wild flowers are pretty
So are wild kittens
Colourful palm trees
Sway in the breeze
Parrots glide
But I hide!

Laura Bradley (9)
Martley Primary School, Martley

England Vs Brazil

Brazil is winning
The crowd is singing
England's scoring
The match is getting boring
The crowd is looking
The ref is booking
And England have won the match.

James Clough (9)
Mordiford CE Primary School, Mordiford

The Welsh Rugby Team

I find the Welsh team great.
I feel like they're my mates.
I love it when Golden Boots gets a long try and shoots.
All the team is tough, beefy and tall
And to the opposite teams they're cruel.
They have a top defence,
Won lots of games, this must be their tenth.
So *go Wales!*

Bryony Rogers (10)
Mordiford CE Primary School, Mordiford

Stripe

I've got a pet guinea pig called Stripe,
When he got ill he gave me a fright.
Running round like crazy,
After being so lazy,
Going like the speed of light.

Evie Gullis (10)
Mordiford CE Primary School, Mordiford

Jabbermockery

(Based on 'Jabberwocky' by Lewis Carroll)

'Twas Monday and the fat boys
Did twist and turn in the lunch hall.
All mimsy was the lunch lady
And the food was cool.

Beware the hall monitor my pal,
His tickets which snarl, his microphone that shouts
Beware the headmaster and shun
The evil bullies

He took his lunchbox in hand
Long time it took to reach the toilet
So he sat and rested by the floor
And sat an hour in thought.

And as in sweet thought he stood,
The hall monitor came with steps which shatter
Bang! Slam! went the lunchbox
He went wobbling back.

And hast thou passed the hall monitor?
'Yes, come Billy, come join our gang.'
'Oh, frabjous day, yippee, hooray,'
He laughed in his joy.

'Twas Monday and the fat boys
Did twist and turn in the lunch hall,
All mimsy was the lunch lady
And the food was cool.

Will Price (10)
Mordiford CE Primary School, Mordiford

Quad Biking

B e extreme push yourself to the limit
I n wheel spinning conditions
K ick start your bike
E ngine hot so do not touch.

Will Pritchard (10)
Mordiford CE Primary School, Mordiford

Attack Of Mars

Floating spaceships going into battle
Charging heavily like a herd of cattle
Charging into Mars, a planet in space
Showing the aliens not to mess with the human race
The fight is nearly over, they've had a big loss
They shouldn't have attacked us,
We're showing them who's boss
They're fleeing like cowards
We've got them in the run
A couple more aliens to get the job done.

Tom Taylor (11)
Mordiford CE Primary School, Mordiford

Super Zero

My arms are floppy and skinny like a stick,
Life is horrible when you're truly thick.

I've got no money; I've got no fans,
I've got no spinach I have to do with jam.

My head is like a blocked drain,
It really is a bit of a pain.

I really feel kind of silly,
Even now Mum says I'm like a lily.

I feel sick, like a mouldy shoe,
I wish I could be born again brand new.

Heidi Jackson (11)
Mordiford CE Primary School, Mordiford

Space And Mars

S pace has got a planet Mars,
P eople never visit Mars,
A nd there was a volcano erupting,
C ould you see a horrifying sight?
E ven an explosion people are wondering.

A valanches of lava explode out of the volcano,
N ever go to Mars, never go to Mars,
D evastating lava flows through the night.

M ars is exploding with lava,
A nd hot burning rocks,
R ed steaming lava running down Mars,
S o we are wondering, what will happen to Mars in the future?

Ashley Stanton (10)
Mordiford CE Primary School, Mordiford

Skiing

People racing down the slopes,
Snow spraying over everyone.
Lifts going up and down,
Millions of people having fun.

Learning children falling over,
Skis sliding under their feet.
Screaming children up on chairlifts,
Brilliant skiers looking neat.

Groups skiing down slopes,
The last time before they go back.
So it's the end of their holiday
They go back to their chalet to pack.

Lucy Abbiss (11)
Mordiford CE Primary School, Mordiford

Midnight

Tick-tock goes the clock,
Midnight's very near.
The moon's shining like a diamond,
Midnight's almost here.

Dogs barking by the gate,
Thinking midnight's great.
People all in their beds,
Surely midnight's here.

Fireflies buzzing in the air,
Playing in the midnight sky.
Flowers sleeping in the ground,
Because midnight's almost here.

Stars twinkling in the sky,
Midnight's so, so clear.
Tick-tock goes the clock,
Finally midnight's here.

Alison Gardner (10)
Mordiford CE Primary School, Mordiford

Snow

Snow, snow, snow
White and fluffy
Cold, cold, cold
Funny, funny, funny
Falls from the sky
From high above
Look at it fall
Snow, snow, snow
White and fluffy
Cold, cold, cold
Funny, funny, funny.

Sarah Scotford (9)
Mordiford CE Primary School, Mordiford

My Pets

I have a dog called Alfie,
He's very, very furry.
He can get very muddy
And make Mum fill up with fury!

I have a rabbit called Harvey,
He's very blacky and whitey.
He's really, really lovely
And sometimes can be bitey!

I have a rabbit called Hector,
He's very, very fluffy.
He's my matey, matey, matey
And his fur is very puffy!

I have 3 fishy fishes,
They're in my pondy, pondy.
They're creamy and goldy
And very, very fondy!

I had a bunny called Thumper,
He was whitey and patchy.
He was the besty, besty, besty
And never bitey or scratchy!

Hannah Goulding (11)
Mordiford CE Primary School, Mordiford

My Bedroom

M y bedroom is very messy,
Y ellow curtains ripped.

B ed is never made,
E verything's been flipped,
D ictionary's binned,
R oom roaring,
O ranges been splatted against the wall,
O ver the bed and over the floor,
M y bedroom is very messy.

Harry Abbiss (9)
Mordiford CE Primary School, Mordiford

The Water Cycle

The thing that we make,
Out of wind, out of lake,
Is the journey a raindrop must take.

We come to the stream,
Of sin and redeem,
That flows slow and swift like a dream.

Now evaporation,
To cause the creation,
The raindrop condenses to rain.

Now water vapour,
Of water and paper,
The raindrop makes way to a cloud.

The precipitation,
Of the rain's jubilation,
The raindrop doesn't yet end its song!

Benjamin Turner (10)
Mordiford CE Primary School, Mordiford

A Dream I Had

I had a dream
It was so cool
A dragon was destroying our school
And then came in the football team
But they gave out a girly scream
I laughed so hard that I woke up
But I didn't want to - what bad luck
I went to school the very next day
But the school was burnt and closed
Hooray!

Charlie Hodges (11)
Mordiford CE Primary School, Mordiford

My Brothers

My brother is crazy
My brother is lazy
He lies in bed
And fills his head
He lies in bed all morn
And gets out at dawn.

My other brother goes crazy
He is not lazy
There's no doubt
He'll dash about
He gets so red
And won't go to bed
As my brother gets faster
He's more of a disaster.

My brother who's lazy
Does not go crazy
He reads a bit
He sleeps a bit
There is no doubt
My brother won't get out
Except for food and drink.

My other brother
Does not bother
The only time he's calm
Is when he's in alarm
He hates schools
He hates rules
My little brother does not think!

Julia Bijl (9)
Northleigh CE Primary School, Malvern

Zebras

Zebras are stripy,
They are very scruffy and knotty,
They have lots of flies in their fur and their eyes
And they tend to have spots.
Some run free in the wild. *Bump, bump,* they go on the ground.
They have to be careful because the lions and other big cats
will eat them.
They run as fast as they can and jump over bushes.
They run very fast,
And that is a few things about zebras.

Niamh Canning (7)
Northleigh CE Primary School, Malvern

Pollution

G lobal warming is dangerous,
L ow aeroplanes will have a suffering engine,
O rdinary batteries don't have pollution,
B ad things will happen
A t different times.
L eave the world in peace.

W hat are we going to do
A bout this coming disaster
R eady to spoil our planet?
N ow we must take care
I n every way we can.
N othing should be left to chance,
G et it right now.

Morgan David Mason (7)
Northleigh CE Primary School, Malvern

About Me

I am very fond of my blonde hair.
I have blue eyes. I like to share and have fun with my friends.

I have some guinea pigs called Britney and Faye,
they like to eat straw and they like to eat hay.

I have two sisters called Laura and Beth and a brother called Dan.
I like to play with them when I am OK.

I got to bed at 8 o'clock and wake up at 7 o'clock,
I go to school every day and I have a little play every day.

I live with my mum and I go to my dad's every weekend,
I like to eat ice cream and other things.

Lucy Constable (9)
Northleigh CE Primary School, Malvern

Snowy Days

Snow, snow all around,
everywhere falling to the ground.
It's everywhere, even in your hair,
falling from the trees down
even in the little town.
Everyone's throwing snowballs at you,
don't you just love it, I do too!
Snow, snow all around,
everywhere falling to the ground.

It's clean and white
before a snowball fight.
You see snow all around,
people making patterns on the ground.

Snow, I love it, yahoo!
I hope you like it too.

Snow, snow all around,
everywhere falling to the ground!

Kali Williams (8)
Northleigh CE Primary School, Malvern

Autumn

Autumn is coming,
autumn is coming,
leaves are turning bright colours
just in a flash,
wind is coming, swirling round
very fast,
all the green from the leaves
is turning orange and browny-red and yellow,
squirrels are collecting their nuts.

And then it is autumn.

Emma Dawson (7)
Northleigh CE Primary School, Malvern

Skateboarding Way

Skateboarding down my way
Through parks and city streets
Flying through the air.

Fraser Savage (7)
Northleigh CE Primary School, Malvern

My Poem

Around about the frosty go,
In and out there we go,
skidding around on ice blades,
slipping over and over again.
Skiing faster and faster we go,
people crashing because of you,
Snowboarding down and down,
there we go. Oh no - a tree I see.
Crash! Crash!

Ross Mulka (8)
Northleigh CE Primary School, Malvern

Animals In Distress

A penguin comes to the shore
And clings desperately to dry land,
She pulls herself upright,
Struggling and weak.

For she is covered from head to foot in
Black, sticky oil that was poured into the sea,
Thoughtlessly by mankind.

She stays still for a moment,
Glancing around helplessly.
But sadly she is alone,
And her fate is yet to come.

Then she collapses and stays there
For the next few hours,
As her legs are not stable enough to hold her.

Her death is slow and painful,
Then she takes her last breath
And closes her eyes heavily.

Katherine Stokes (10)
Northleigh CE Primary School, Malvern

Just A Tanka . . . Or Is It?

Trees howl in the dark,
The wind blows outside my door,
There's no need to fear,
'Hearts will freeze,' whispers the breeze,
Spirits come hither no more!

Rowan Hayes (10)
Northleigh CE Primary School, Malvern

A Rabbit

One morning I looked out my window
I saw a white figure,
it was whitey-grey and very timid,
it ran in a flash and I didn't really see.
I rushed downstairs
and went outside.
I looked around
left, right, up, down, side to side . . .
then suddenly I turned around
and there, right in front of me,
was a little, white rabbit.
I bent down slowly and put my hand out,
then it walked a bit closer.
Then it jumped on my knee.
So that is my poem about the little white rabbit.

Skye Hope Gamble (9)
Northleigh CE Primary School, Malvern

My Own Poem

C is for caring and being careful,
A is for always admitting the truth,
M is for magical and making nice things for my friends,
E is for everything I do is excellent,
R is for a rare child to get,
O is for obeying other children and adults,
N is for not being nervous, and doing things well.

H is for being happy all the time,
E is for my ears are listening all the time,
A is for being able to do most things,
T is for trying my best in every lesson,
O is for out of the world child I am,
N is for a never dull child I am with someone else.

Cameron Heaton (8)
Northleigh CE Primary School, Malvern

Why?

Why have the white people raided our land
Where once the shamans used to stand?
Why have they come and destroyed our trees
And polluted our clear, fresh forest breeze?
Why have they killed the bird and the bear
And left us only to stand and stare?
Why have they shot us and left us to suffer,
For it does not make them any tougher?
Why do they carry weapons of war
So there is no peace anymore?
Why do they take all our supplies,
For they know that we will all die?
Why do they bring creatures from Heaven
And force them to help cause death and mayhem?
Nature was not made to be used for war
And we will not tolerate any more!

Isobel Mathias (10)
Northleigh CE Primary School, Malvern

Who Am I?

I have slimy scales and I am a terrifying creature,
I am the king of the ocean,
My head is the same shape as a hammer.
I am feared a lot, especially by small fish.
I have sharp teeth and people keep them as fossils.
I could just about fit a whole human in my mouth.
I am usually black or blue, or even grey.

A: Hammerhead shark.

Luke Stanton (11)
Northleigh CE Primary School, Malvern

A Bedtime Story

(Inspired by the fairy tale, 'Red Riding Hood'
In the style of 'Revolting Rhymes' by Roald Dahl)

The little girl in red
Was pestered.
Granny's ill, forgot her pill,
We pestered her, we did.
Now her hair is vile green;
And her nails are black; never are clean.
Her skin is yellow: nose is bent.
And girlie in red, with cookies is sent,
To deliver cookies to the wild thing;
The one with the hair and the metre bum sting.

The young 'un skips, but sadly she trips
and the big dog Wolfie comes out.
'Where are you going with cookies so sweet?'
Says girl: 'These are for my granny to eat.'
'So,' says the wolf with a grin on his face,
'Where is your grandma? Number of the place?'
Ruby gown then shouts, '103!'
Wolf replies,
'That's helpful to me!'

So Riding Hood skips down Meadowy Lane,
The wolf takes a short cut: ever the same
And arrives there first, says, 'Hi,' to Grandma,
Granny turns and croaks, 'And you are?'
The wolf grunts and says, 'Don't wanna eat her.'
But he does! He does! Without a stir!
And Wolfie, dressed in nightie, lies in bed:
He pulls a shower cap over his head.

Ruby Gown comes, opens the door:
Yells, 'Hi Gran!' with a boisterous roar:
Hoodie skips to bed, looks him in the face:
Says, 'Dear Gran! You're a disgrace!'
And goes through the usual remarks;
And the wolf's eyes, they flutter, they spark.
He bares his teeth, jumps out of bed;
runs into the door and *bump!* in his head!
Hoodie phones home, dials woodcutter:
Woody charges along, dives and cuts 'her'!

Granny comes out, and Wolfie is dead!
So now let us all settle to bed.

Emma Knowles (10)
Northleigh CE Primary School, Malvern

Snowflakes

As snowflakes fell down from the sky,
One in particular caught my eye.
Silvery white,
Glittered with ice,
Delicate, fragile,
Magical and nice!

Softly landing on my face,
Disappearing without a trace . . .

Sophie Cornelius (11)
Northleigh CE Primary School, Malvern

Hooray For Rooney!

Straight through the defence,
He's clean through, he's got to score!
Dropped onto his foot,
Wow! What a brilliant shot,
It's in! Hooray for Rooney!

Jared Maxfield (10)
Northleigh CE Primary School, Malvern

My Mischievous Pet - Tanka

Poppy is a cat.
She's a mischievous cat,
She tries to scratch you.
Poppy's eyes, like a tiger's,
She has paws like a lion.

Amie Bradshaw (10)
Northleigh CE Primary School, Malvern

Skiing Down The Icy Mountain - Tanka

Skiing down the slopes
While the chill of the white wind
Slaps your frozen face
As you fly down the mountain
Your adrenaline pumping.

James Merley (10)
Northleigh CE Primary School, Malvern

Mum

My mum is the best,
she is cooler than the rest.
She does never screech
but she does not like a leech.
I think that she overall,
is the best mum of them all.

Eric Carlen (11)
Northleigh CE Primary School, Malvern

Football

F ootball is the best game in the world,
O -O at the start of the game. It's electric as the whistle blows.
O ff they go. The whistle is blown. It's the best game.
T he stands are high but I don't care. I'm not afraid of heights.
B all is passed to each player again and again.
A ll first half there's passing. It's getting quite boring.
    Suddenly we score!
L ike a bullet it goes to the back of the net,
L ast second of the match 1-0. We are at the top of the league
    till next time.

Joe Whitehouse (8)
Northleigh CE Primary School, Malvern

Happiness

Happiness is golden like the bright, shining sun,
Happiness smells like the first flowers of spring,
Happiness tastes like sweet, melted chocolate,
Happiness feels like an explosion of laughter,
Happiness is like a baby's first step,
Happiness reminds me of my mum.

Kate Richards (9)
Northleigh CE Primary School, Malvern

Dreams

Dreams are like a nameless horseman cantering up a sand dune,
They feel like a story of thoughts and emotions,
And in those thoughts and emotions you can see your happiest day,
You can feel your angriest thought.
When you are dreaming you are in a world of your own,
A world of your own where no one can harm you.

Frankie Shackleton (9)
Northleigh CE Primary School, Malvern

Who Am I?

I enjoy eating dormice on a cold winter's night,
My bite is deadly venomous,
I can be extremely dangerous,
I have a tongue like a stretched fork,
I use my scales to move across the ground,
I enjoy slithering up tall trees,
I come in all shapes, sizes and colours,
I live in many different habitats,
I sometimes live in the jungles of Africa,
I enjoy living in swamps and rivers,
I can live in cold countries and hot,
One of my species can rattle their tails,
I hiss!

Who am I?

Charlotte Jakeman (10)
Northleigh CE Primary School, Malvern

We Break Up, We Break Down

We break up, we break down,
We don't care if the school falls down,
This time next week where shall we be?
Out of the gates of misery.
No more Latin, no more French,
No more sitting on the old, hard bench.
No more cabbages filled with slugs,
No more drinking out of dirty, old mugs.
No more spiders in my tea
Making googly eyes at me.
Kick up the tables,
Kick up the chairs.

Mia Alford (9)
Northleigh CE Primary School, Malvern

A Graveyard - Renga

Alone in the sky,
Up above me so, so high,
Silver through the mist.

Mist is in graveyards,
And other sad, lonely lands,
As if it were death.

Graves scattered around,
Mist creeping over the ground,
Silent and eerie.

Silent as the dead,
That's what the people say, though -
Are the dead silent?

Non-breathing, silent,
Lying dead below a grave,
Or is it that way?

We all need to breathe,
Well, of course, apart from ghosts -
If there were such things.

Silvery, ghostly,
Not dead, but still not alive,
Silver spirits, death.

Mary Fleming (11)
Northleigh CE Primary School, Malvern

My Teacher

When I'm feeling down
When I'm feeling bad
My teacher cheers me up
And then I'm feeling glad.

Zoë McKerr (8)
Northleigh CE Primary School, Malvern

My Dog

My dog is jolly and playful,
he's got a loving heart.
He's been such a cutie,
right from the start.

He sleeps in the utility room
where it's nice and cosy,
and when I go to give him a hug,
my cheeks go red and rosy.

My mum and I take him for walks
on the common with green grass.
I throw the frisbee for him,
and lots of other dogs pass.

I give him two scoops of food for breakfast
and teatime too.
When he was little we would say, 'Busy, busy,'
and then he would go to the loo.

I love my dog so much,
and I'll love him forever,
he's better than any other dog
even if you put them all together.

Laura Sockett (9)
Northleigh CE Primary School, Malvern

Winter's Coming

Winter's frost and glistening snow,
crystal icicles hang down low.
The moon comes up in the dark, black sky,
the stars all twinkle way up high.
A sparkling white blanket covers the ground,
as winter comes creeping without a sound.
When frost comes sliding through,
the ice on the ground turns from silver to blue.

Alexandra Garwood Walker (8)
Northleigh CE Primary School, Malvern

Birthdays

Birthdays, my birthday's really near,
the time of my life,
the day I was born.
I wonder what I'll get,
chocolate, sweets, candy or more.
Birthdays are special, especially for you.
celebrating your birth, your youth, your life.
Every year you have a birthday,
one year older.
Then the day comes,
your birthday, opening presents, having fun.
Then the party,
how exciting.
Just have to wait until next year!

Isabel Ellis (9)
Northleigh CE Primary School, Malvern

Spring Has Come

It's snow again, oh what bliss!
But the trees and flowers; it's summer I miss,
Though spring is looming in the mist.

The nights are dark and very cold,
The weeks go by, I'm getting old,
But spring is here, or so I'm told.

The morning's light, the air is clear,
There're baby cows and baby deer,
And spring is here,
Oh, spring is here!

Alexandra Smith (10)
Northleigh CE Primary School, Malvern

My Little Baby Brother

My little baby brother,
Dancing in the zoo,
Down falls his nappy,
Ewoooo.
Everyone is staring,
People cover their eyes,
All the girls are screaming,
People try to look at pies.
Mum's trying to change him,
Take him into the loo,
5 minutes later, he's running around the zoo.
20 minutes later, nappy's got more weight.
30 minutes later, here we go again!

Charlie Bytheway (10)
Northleigh CE Primary School, Malvern

The Day I Had A Dream

Home,
My home,
The home of a free man,
But something told me it wasn't
And this was Rome,
This was my old home,
The home of a free man,
Was this reality?
I doubted it,
I woke up
And saw what I had become,
The gladiator!

Kieran Jeffrey (10)
Northleigh CE Primary School, Malvern

The Garden Is Changing Its Clothes

It is summer and the garden is changing its clothes,
From snowdrop dresses to sunflower swimsuits.
It is summer and the garden is changing its clothes,
Foxgloves no longer, now bluebells for summer.
The garden is changing its clothes,
The sharp petalled roses gleam in the sun,
It is summer now, winter is over and done.
It is summer and the garden is changing its clothes,
Daisies are summer, snowdrops are winter,
The garden is changing its clothes.

Now it is winter and the garden is changing its clothes,
Bluebells no longer now foxgloves for winter.
The garden is changing its clothes,
The sharp petalled roses don't gleam in the sun,
It is winter now, summer is over and done.
It is winter and the garden is changing its clothes,
Snowdrops are winter and daisies are summer.
The garden is changing its clothes,
Now it is spring and the garden is changing,
Oh you know how it goes!

Jessica Smith (10)
Northleigh CE Primary School, Malvern

The Rescued Horse

Running wild, running free,
Running through the fields happily,
I have a stable,
I have lots to eat,
I have lots of friends,
And even more to meet,
I really, really love it here,
Now I never cry a tear,
What happiness and joy it brings,
Living here at *Redwings!*

Sophie Dawson (11)
Northleigh CE Primary School, Malvern

The Inter-Galactic Sheep

There was once a sheep
Who wanted to keep
A world record for flying to Saturn
So he made a small space shuttle
I think it was subtle enough to hold two
And he found a friend called Betty Kung Fu
To go in his spaceship for two.
So they started it, how it went *zoom!*
They broke the world record, they were very happy
And were greeted by their friend, Von Kappy.
He gave them presents of toothpaste, hee-hee
And then he gave them a small killer bee
Whose name was Declan, Declan is me.

Declan Amphlett (8)
Northleigh CE Primary School, Malvern

Presents

Presents are like a magic show,
What's inside? You do not know.
It might be balls, it might be bats,
It might even be a fluffy, little cat!
It could be pencils, it could be pens,
It could even be Big Ben!
Presents feel exciting and surprising,
They taste like a mysterious ice cream,
Presents look like a ride that makes you scream with excitement,
They sound like laughter and fun
And that's why I like presents!

Gemma James (9)
Northleigh CE Primary School, Malvern

Ice

Ice is cold like an icy cold wind in December,
If you lick it, your tongue will freeze, become numb and never
move again,
It smells like the damp in the bus shelter down the road,
It tastes sweet but one wrong move and it's as sour as a bitter lemon,
Clothes damp, hair wet, socks drenched, nose blocked, like the
worst cold you've ever had.
That's what I feel when I touch ice.
It reminds me of a ghost-like creature grabbing me by the arm,
Ice sends a shiver down my spine.

Amy Straughan (9)
Northleigh CE Primary School, Malvern

The Noise In The Rainforest

I was in the rainforest, rainforest, rainforest,
I was awake in my tent at night, at night, at night
and I heard a noise, a noise, a noise.
I crept outside, outside, outside,
I went round the tent, the tent, the tent,
I found an anteater, an anteater, an anteater,
I crept back into bed, to bed, to bed,
Then I fell asleep, *zzzzzzz*.

Stuart Hawkins (9)
Northleigh CE Primary School, Malvern

Guilt

Guilt is black like an overhanging shadow,
It feels as cold as ice over your head,
It sounds like the screams coming from a tomb.
It tastes as sharp as a deathly long knife,
It reminds me of when blood was spilt.

Jamie MacKenzie (9)
Northleigh CE Primary School, Malvern

Summer

Summer is like a long-lost dream, finally discovered.
It lifts the dull sheet of winter away to be used another day.
Summer tastes like a full jar of sweets, soon in my belly.
It smells like freshly picked lilies.
It looks like a cottage decorated with flowers and bright colours.
Summer sounds like children's laughter.
Summer feels like going to a different country.
Summer reminds me of my favourite places.

Catherine Fleming (9)
Northleigh CE Primary School, Malvern

The Sun

The sun is a flame, flickering high above us
It brings light to our world as we call the day.
It melts the winter snow that traps us inside
So we can come out to play!

The sun looks like a football kicked in outer space
It feels like sticking your hand right into a fire
It sounds like a flame swaying in the wind
It smells like . . . an old car tyre!

Heidi Loveridge (9)
Northleigh CE Primary School, Malvern

Thought

Thought is a colour so pale, so blue,
So amazing, so soft, so wonderful.
Thought makes you feel like you're floating, dreaming,
Singing with not a care in the world.
Thought tastes, thought feels like marshmallows, fresh,
                                        tasty and smooth.
Thought is fluffy and white, just like snow,
But as warm and as special as your mum's home-made cakes.

Hannah Kenyon (10)
Northleigh CE Primary School, Malvern

It Is Winter And The Garden Is Changing . . .

It is winter and the garden is changing its clothes
Ripping off its short sleeved leaf shirts
And pulling up its brick-like shoes
Wrapping itself up in mud jackets, shoving on foxgloves
All nice things gone now, sad and damp wherever you go
The nice, spiky rose petals now crisp and dry
Now the cold wet puddles fill the flower beds
It is winter and the garden is changing its clothes
There are no sunny times anymore, just time to die away.

Zoë Burbeck (9)
Northleigh CE Primary School, Malvern

Unicorn Dreams

U nicorns are lovely animals
N ice animals,
I love them, they're my favourite animals
'C ause they're magical but not real.
O range, purple, red, blue, white, black
R uby is my unicorn's name
N aughty and cheeky sometimes.

D reams, I have a lot about unicorns
R uby is a kind unicorn
E very unicorn's kind
A nd cheeky
M agic they are
S eriously magic.

Lucy Cooper (9)
Northleigh CE Primary School, Malvern

Creatures

Hedgehog moving down the road
All those spikes what a big load.
I went down to the double-decker bus
Right there was a big, big fuss.
Sat in a seat and had some strong cheese
Bumped into an old cow who fell on its knees.
I went forward, saw a small puss
Then was surprised to see a stegosaurus.
I jumped up in shock
To see a whole flock.

Ben Jones (8)
Northleigh CE Primary School, Malvern

Global Warming

We all know about global warming
And that the ice caps are not forming
It is probable that it'll become unstoppable
The ice caps are melting
The people who make pollution should get a good pelting
We all know that global warming is here
And that the end is near.

Jake Stromqvist (9)
Northleigh CE Primary School, Malvern

Anger

Anger tastes so sweet,
Anger is bright red,
Anger feels so strong,
Anger smells a lot like steam,
Anger sounds like an exploding bomb,
Anger comes when I am annoyed.

Rhys Alyn Griffiths (9)
Northleigh CE Primary School, Malvern

My Cat

My cat is . . .
A cute bundle stuffed with fluff.

My cat is . . .
A roly-poly, curled up,
rounded puffed pompom.

My cat is . . .
Scratchy, scratchy, scratchy cat
Purry, furry, ping-pong ball.

Jordan Heudebourck-Rice (7)
Northleigh CE Primary School, Malvern

Revenge

Revenge is bright red
It feels like a hot iron burning
It tastes sweet and strong
It sounds like broth bubbling
Hotter till it explodes and spills everywhere.
It smells like a distant smell beckoning
It reminds me of my fists.

Jeremy Bijl (9)
Northleigh CE Primary School, Malvern

Mermaids

M ermaids live in the sea
E ating shells up, 1, 2, 3.
R emember not to scare them
M ermaids get frightened
A nd when they sing their song
I t sometimes sounds like ding, dang, dong.
D awn will come soon
S ome time after the light of the moon.

Ellie Cornelius (8)
Northleigh CE Primary School, Malvern

Favies

I have lots of favies
One of them is babies

Football is the best
It is a bit above the rest

But the best thing is going on holiday
And when we do we come back in May.

Maxwell Bytheway (7)
Northleigh CE Primary School, Malvern

Hamster

H ow much do you like hamsters?
A pet that lives for 2 years
M y hamster
S o soft
T wo years
E eekkk
R eally want one!

Jacob Lambon (8)
Northleigh CE Primary School, Malvern

Seasons

Summer is hot,
it makes me sweat a lot.
Autumn is cool,
it shines like a jewel.
Winter is fresh,
re-awakening the world's flesh.
Spring is new life,
animals find a wife.

Ruth Stromqvist (9)
Northleigh CE Primary School, Malvern

The Animal Poem

Bunnies are funny
Honey is bears' stuff
Hyenas are nasty
Cheetahs are fasty
Anteaters are big lickers
Velociraptors are cool flickers
A tall brachiosaurus
Could break a small mall.

Charlie Onions (8)
Northleigh CE Primary School, Malvern

My Three Pets

I have three pets called George, Jake and Moonlight
They are very nice and furry
They're really fun and sometimes I think I'm in Heaven
I take my dog to the common
I feed my cat every day
I play with my hamster every week
I am so happy with my pets
I think I'm in sweetie land!

Rosie Milner (8)
Northleigh CE Primary School, Malvern

Anger

Anger is the colour of a lit-up fire
Anger sounds like the roar of a dragon
Like a roar of a lion catching his prey.
Anger smells like a bonfire burning
Like a house burning down
Anger feels like a broken piece of glass.
It tastes like a red-hot chilli catching on fire in my mouth
Anger reminds me of when me and my friends fall out.

Rebecca Lockton (9)
Northleigh CE Primary School, Malvern

Anger

It feels like a devil burning in your throat
It feels like fire in your head
It feels like your head is going to explode
It tastes like raw onions in your tummy
It is horrible
Anger.

Chris Need (7)
Northleigh CE Primary School, Malvern

Katie

K ind and cuddly Katie
A nd I love her
T ogether we take her to school
I 'm always taking her to bed with me
E very day with her is a very special day.

Gary O'Callaghan (7)
Northleigh CE Primary School, Malvern

Seasons

Winter is cold, very, very cold
It's like being wrapped in a fold of ice.
It's like being wrapped in a layer of snow.
Spring is warm - very, very warm
It's like being wrapped in a fold of fire.
Summer is hot - very, very hot
It's like being wrapped in a layer of sun.
Autumn is chilly - very, very chilly
It's like being wrapped in a layer of wind.

Annabel Pearson (8)
Northleigh CE Primary School, Malvern

Animals

A tiger is the colour of a sunflower.
The tiger's sound is like a roar flowing through the wind.
A tiger's taste is like a wild berry growing on the bush.
The tiger's smell is like a fire burning up into the air.
The tiger feels like a warm teddy.
It reminds me of India.

Amara Devi (8)
Northleigh CE Primary School, Malvern

Love

Love is the colour of pinky-white.
Love is the smell of expensive perfume.
Love is the taste of strawberry candy.
Love feels like precious gold.
Love reminds me of my mum.

Lucy Ellaway-Bell (8)
Northleigh CE Primary School, Malvern

Happiness

H appiness reminds me of children laughing
A ugust is when my teacher's birthday is
P eople smile at me and I wave back
P olar is my favourite bear
I cing is my favourite topping
N ovember is my favourite month
E very day is a happy day
S eptember is my birthday
S unday is my best day of the week.

Harriet Walker (9)
Northleigh CE Primary School, Malvern

Anger

Anger is red like fireballs.
It feels like red-hot chilli peppers.
It tastes like pepper.
It sounds like a baby screaming in your ear.
It smells like ashes burning in the fire.
It reminds me of the sun.

Luke Maisey (8)
Northleigh CE Primary School, Malvern

What Am I?

I look like a sphere
I tell a lot of geography
I show countries with names
I spin like a wheel
I even have your best countries on me
I show towns and cities also
What am I?

Ethan Bristow (9)
Northleigh CE Primary School, Malvern

Anger

Anger is the worst thing you can have
It smells like exploding trains
Sometimes it feels like someone getting cut
The colour is the colour of a fire burning
It tastes of burnt pizza
It reminds me of my sister.

Noah Thompson (7)
Northleigh CE Primary School, Malvern

Anger

Anger is red like burning-hot lava
It tastes like fiery chilli peppers
It feels like fire flames all over me
It sounds like a train
It smells like gas
It reminds me of kicking my brother
And making him cry.

Aaron Boden (7)
Northleigh CE Primary School, Malvern

Saint Valentine

Valentine is the colour of red and blue
It feels so soft, so smooth
It tastes like sugar
It sounds like birds singing
It smells like sugar, like love
It reminds me of love and that is right.

Laura Dixon (8)
Northleigh CE Primary School, Malvern

Anger

Anger feels like a burning hot iron
Anger tastes like chillies that've come out of the oven
Anger looks like fire coming out of the fireplace
Anger sounds like me getting out of bed in the morning
Because someone has been knocking on my door
And that's not pleasant
Anger smells like the bonfire in the field next to my house
Anger reminds me of fighting with my brother.

Laurie Essenhigh (7)
Northleigh CE Primary School, Malvern

Luke

There once was a spook, whose name was Luke
He went to the fair and ate an eclair
He scared the Queen who was very mean
She hit him hard and made him eat lard
He grew fat and wore a hat
Luke died and everyone cried
So that is the story of Luke the spook.

Amy Campbell (10)
Our Lady's Catholic Primary School, Alcester

My Friends

My friends are the best ever
Amy, Hannah, Becky and Heather.
They give me necklaces and take me into town,
They also bought me a gold crown.

My friends are the best ever
Samantha, Sally, Sarah and Emma.
Rachel is the best of all
She has just taken me to a ball
My friends are the best ever
I'll never forget my friends, no, not ever.

Kimberly Badoud (10)
Our Lady's Catholic Primary School, Alcester

Winter

W e all love winter
I n the snow we play
N ebula in the sky
T ightly cuddled in bed
E fface all the ice
R unning in the cold.

Kristi Kelly (10)
Our Lady's Catholic Primary School, Alcester

Jill Malone

Once there was a girl called Jill
Who always was so ill
So one day someone made a curse
And that someone was a nurse.

The only cure was to swim in the sea
After having baked potatoes for tea
So one day after doing just that
(Having baked potatoes for her tea)
She ran all the way down to the salty sea.

Through sand, little puddles, lakes galore
She ran right down to the sandy shore.

At last she was free of the curse
But she hadn't bargained for something much worse
She swam right into the jaws of a shark
Who swallowed her like a little lark.

PS; That was the end of the girl called Jill.

Becky Cunningham (10)
Our Lady's Catholic Primary School, Alcester

My Room Is A Mess

My room is a mess
I haven't hung up my dress
There are toys everywhere
I can't find my teddy bear
I haven't Hoovered the floor
'Cause Hoovering's a bore
My brother messed up my bed
So I whacked him on the head
My mum started shouting
And I started pouting
My room's not the best
Because it is a *big mess!*

Hannah Campbell (10)
Our Lady's Catholic Primary School, Alcester

My Pets

I have a pet rat
His name is Scat
He sits on the rug all day
Even the cat doesn't scare him away!
Mind you, this cat
Is even lazier than Scat.

I also have a dog called Bud
He likes to roll in the mud
His best friend is a budgie called Ben
Whose talent is writing with a pen.
Bud's favourite meal is roasted spud -
That's much worse than rolling in mud.

My pets are the best you can clearly see
Scat rat, Bud, Ben and me!
(By the way, have I mentioned Spike my pet dragon . . . ?)

Rachel Hendry (11)
Our Lady's Catholic Primary School, Alcester

Birds

Birds are all around us
Birds are in the air
Birds are on the ground
For birds, come on, we care.

Birds are part of nature
Birds are birds of prey
When they are old enough
They sit down and lay.

The cycle then repeats itself
But I don't have time to say it again
Just off now to go inside
Now the bird's dead, it's tea time for Wayne (the cat!)

Daniel O'Neill (9)
Our Lady's Catholic Primary School, Alcester

School Dinners

Bold carrots
Plump parrots
Lumpy mash
We have to pay cash
Chicken in gravy
All green and navy.

Oh the smell
I'd rather go to Hell
Green cabbage
All carried in a baggage
Potatoes all yellow and round
Splat! it goes on the ground.

Yellow, pink, white and brown
All shaped like a clown
Plop! onto the plate
All in a state
We don't like school dinners
Throw them into the black binners.

Sarah O'Reilly (10)
Our Lady's Catholic Primary School, Alcester

Friends

My friends are so great,
They work themselves a treat.
Always being there for me,
Oh, they are so sweet.

They invited me for tea
The food was delicious on our plate.
We were definitely having a fantastic time,
My friends are so great.

Samantha Preece (11)
Our Lady's Catholic Primary School, Alcester

The Beach

I strolled along the beach
The sand swept along my feet
I sat down and looked into the ocean
And rubbed myself with sun lotion
I licked my lips at the glistening ice cream
And before I knew it I was in a dream.

I ran along the shore
And played with a bouncy ball
I walked along by the palm trees
And feel the nice cool breeze
I gave a smile and within a mile
I took a great leap onto the warm, sunny beach!

Charlie Stanley (11)
Our Lady's Catholic Primary School, Alcester

My Garden

The garden is full of colours
Buddleia trees and others
The wind blows the trees
It's blowing a breeze.

In the summer bees buzz
And butterflies flutter
A sweet smell of pollen
From all the plants
And when I'm in bed
They all start to dance.

And when I wake up the very next day
All the flowers swing and sway
In the beautiful sun I water them
Before they die out and start to sprout.

Lucie Watson (11)
Our Lady's Catholic Primary School, Alcester

The Grey Horse

There was a grey horse standing silent and sleek
He was on a hill, patient and meek
His mane was long and blowing
His fur was white and flowing
His hooves were black and shiny
His eyes were glistening and tiny
He galloped across the open moors
He could see the distant shores
He jumped over the lapping waves
He trotted over the sand to the open caves.

The horse's tail dragged along a stone
He walked on more and heard a groan
He walked on more and saw sparkles
He stood silent and sleek
He stood on diamonds still and meek
He was the grey horse.

Shannon Hall (11)
Our Lady's Catholic Primary School, Alcester

The Beanstalk

Up to the sky the beanstalk grew and grew
Going straight past the clouds and out of view.
There was a boy called Jack
Who climbed right up to the top.

He found a giant who had plenty of money
So he took the money and ran to his mummy.
Chopped down the beanstalk with his father's axe
That was the end of that.

Lani Duncan (8)
Race Leys Junior School, Bedworth

Mummy

'Is it time to go now Mummy?
I want to have some fun.'
Said Mummy, 'You have to wait dear,
There's so much to be done.'
'The jobs are done now Mummy,
Let's go and have some fun
Mummy, can Daddy come?'

Ellen Smith (7)
Race Leys Junior School, Bedworth

Freaky Friends

Some friends are freaky
And freaky can be peaky.
Some friends are cool
And like splashing in the pool.
My friends are generous and kind
These friends will never fall out of my mind.

Connor Keely (7)
Race Leys Junior School, Bedworth

Vimto Poem

Vimto is yummy
Vimto is for your tummy
It has no fat
It makes me hyper like a rat
It makes my tongue all fizzy
Oh boy it makes me dizzy.

Amy Cadman (11)
Race Leys Junior School, Bedworth

Spooky

Spooky
Shout, 'Trick or treat?'
Spiders hanging from webs
Collecting sweets around the streets,
Scary!

Jordan Randle (10)
Race Leys Junior School, Bedworth

The Kestrel

I was playing in the garden then I see
A kestrel flying in front of me
Its eyes shone silver, feathers chestnut-brown
The most beautiful thing I've seen
The blue tit, robin, crow compares with you
Black, orange, blue, not the colours of you
You may be vicious, a hunter or sly
But you're the master of the sky.

Amy Hawthorne (8)
Race Leys Junior School, Bedworth

Moon Howler Kennings

A moon howler
A silent prowler
A vicious biter
A child frightener
A deadly clawer
A hungry gnawer
A catalogue to make me
A werewolf.

Luke Davis (10)
Race Leys Junior School, Bedworth

Christmas Thank You

(Based on 'Christmas Thank Yous' by Mick Gowar)

Dear Daddy,
Thanks for the BMX
I like the colour blue.
Fancy you putting luminous
Pink stripes all over
That's really nice of you.

George Taylor (10)
Race Leys Junior School, Bedworth

Christmas Thank Yous

(Based on 'Christmas Thank Yous' by Mick Gowar)

Dear Mum,
Thank you for the pottery mug
I've always loved frogs
And fancy buying green and red
My two favourite colours
But I've still got my one with dogs!

Dale Walker (10)
Race Leys Junior School, Bedworth

April Cinquain

Long days
Swimming all day
Flowers grow all around
Girls and boys go outside to play
April.

Danny Kelly (10)
Race Leys Junior School, Bedworth

Quetzalcoatlus - Cinquain

Big wings
A great wingspan
A flying dinosaur
It lived in North America
Toothless.

Josh Greenway (11)
Race Leys Junior School, Bedworth

December Cinquain

Presents
Wake up early
A big tree in the house
Decorations upstairs and down
Christmas.

Lewis Delich (10)
Race Leys Junior School, Bedworth

White Christmas - Cinquain

White frost
Snow on the pane
Freezing cold . . . and so wet
All of the children writing lists
It's fun.

Daniel Vincent (11)
Race Leys Junior School, Bedworth

Christmas Thank You

(Based on 'Christmas Thank Yous' by Mick Gowar)

Dear Auntie,
Thanks for the skirt
The same kind you wear
So you must be
The one in style
And I think you're right
Pink, yellow and orange
It's just lovely to know that
You care.

Amy Harrison (10)
Race Leys Junior School, Bedworth

No School Cinquain

No school
Children playing
Kids on PlayStation 2s
Children playing football outside
More play . . .

Connor Davidson (10)
Race Leys Junior School, Bedworth

About A Baby - Cinquain

Baby
Baby Tayla
To care for you and love
A delivery at Christmas
For us.

Honor Hackett (11)
Race Leys Junior School, Bedworth

The Darkness Of October - Cinquain

Dark, dark
Bags of lollies
Children scare each other
Ghosts walk down the black streets at night
Scream, scream.

Courtney Whittle (10)
Race Leys Junior School, Bedworth

Christmas Thank You

(Based on 'Christmas Thank Yous' by Mick Gowar)

Dear Grandma,
Thank you for the chocolates
They'll be lovely I'm sure
Don't take this the wrong way
But I've decided that first I'm going
To eat the other fifty packets
That are lying on the floor.

Samantha Colley (10)
Race Leys Junior School, Bedworth

Morning - Cinquain

Ringing
Alarm sounds loud
No time to sleep any
Longer, get up, breakfast, clean teeth
School waits.

Ashley Denny (10)
Race Leys Junior School, Bedworth

Christmas Thank Yous

(Based on 'Christmas Thank Yous' by Mick Gowar)

Dear Nan,
Oh what a nice Barbie
The biggest Barbie I adore
And fancy you thinking of
Pink for her clothes
I did love Barbie
When four!

Adele Mellors (10)
Race Leys Junior School, Bedworth

Cinquain

Snow falls
Kids getting toys
People get excited
Turkey, sausage, stuffing, gravy
Christmas.

Thomas Broadaway (10)
Race Leys Junior School, Bedworth

A Scary Cinquain

Scary
Tasty candy
Children's ugly costumes
Dark, spooky and comes once a year
Horror.

Megan Phillips (11)
Race Leys Junior School, Bedworth

A Cinquain For Christmas

Tiptoe
Around the house
Girls and boys are happy
Because the great legend has been
Hooray!

Thomas Flude (11)
Race Leys Junior School, Bedworth

October - Cinquain

Scary!
Lots of candy
Costumes looking spooky
Monsters roaming all of the streets
Trick? Treat?

Shaquille Magee (11)
Race Leys Junior School, Bedworth

October - Cinquain

Scary
Really spooky
Stars getting bright at night
Collecting sweets around the street
Spooky.

Robbie Phillips (10)
Race Leys Junior School, Bedworth

A Cinquain

Horror
Comes once a year
Really, really scary
Going round collecting candy
Screaming.

Mark McKenna (11)
Race Leys Junior School, Bedworth

December - Cinquain

Snowflakes
Stars shining bright
Ripping presents open
Kids making snowmen all around
Christmas.

Hollie O'Callaghan (11)
Race Leys Junior School, Bedworth

Enjoying Holiday - Cinquain

Chilling
Going swimming
Dad is at the barbie
Building a kingdom of castles
Great day!

Sean Hood (11)
Race Leys Junior School, Bedworth

Hallowe'en - Cinquain

Spooky
Trick or treating
Frankenstein and mean ghouls
Children going from door to door
Knocking.

Matthew Rylance (10)
Race Leys Junior School, Bedworth

Me And My Brother

I'm a little boy and I'm called Jake
I've got a pet dog and I'd like a pet snake.

I like drinking pop and eating lovely cake
But if I have too much I'll have bellyache.

Now Travis is my baby brother
He doesn't look like me, he looks like my mother.

He likes to play with all my toys
But he's just not one of us *big boys*.

Jake Gunn (8)
Race Leys Junior School, Bedworth

Spooky Time - Cinquain

Spooky
Delicious sweets
Feeling ill from candy
Walking down the road in the dark
Scary.

Sophie Brain (10)
Race Leys Junior School, Bedworth

Winter

It tastes like a crispy chicken
It smells like warm mince pies
It sounds like bells jingling
It feels like icy fingers running down your spine
Yes, it's winter.

It tastes like hot chocolate
It smells like cold fresh air
It sounds like snow crunching under your feet
It feels like needles digging into you
Yes, it's winter.

It tastes like a warm roast dinner
It smells like wood burning on a fire
It sounds like happy children playing in the snow
It feels like your face is numb
Yes, it's winter.

It tastes like runny, hot chocolate
It smells like Mum's perfume when she hugs you
It sounds like sausages sizzling in the pan
It feels like hailstones hitting you
Yes, it's winter.

Charley Oulton (10)
Race Leys Junior School, Bedworth

Ice - Cinquain

Icy
Slippery roads
The cold snow falling . . . fast
The frost frozen on the rooftops
Careful?

Grace Hood (10)
Race Leys Junior School, Bedworth

Cheerleading

Sunday cheer! Sunday dance!
This is what we like to chant
One, two, we're a crew
Here to entertain you
Spinning kicks, pom-pom shakes
Cartwheels that's all it takes
Football pitch and village green
That's where we can be seen
Carnivals and charity do's
We are here to cheer for you.

Sian Bond (7)
Race Leys Junior School, Bedworth

Love

Love is burgundy red
It smells like blossom
It tastes like strawberry chocolate
It sounds like tinkling bells
It feels like a soft pillow
Love lives in the heart of a rose.

Beth Brindley (9)
Race Leys Junior School, Bedworth

Cinquain

Sparkle!
The bright sticks glow
Round wheels spin so brightly
Waiting in the dark quietly
Crackle!

Cherie Tierney (11)
Race Leys Junior School, Bedworth

The Reader Of This Poem

(Inspired by 'The Writer of this Poem' by Roger McGough)

The reader of this poem
Is as scared as a mouse
As rough as a wall
As tough as a house.

As ugly as can be
As fat as a whale
As sad as an empty hall
As slow as a snail.

As flat as a pancake
As scary as a snake
As boring as a teacher
As annoying as toothache.

'The reader of this poem
Never ceases to amaze
He is one in a billion
(Or so the poem says)'.

Lauren Stokes (10)
Race Leys Junior School, Bedworth

Old Age

Old age is snow white
It smells like an old, dreary house
Old age tastes like sour strawberries
It sounds like raindrops falling softly
It feels like crumbling walls of an old, ancient castle
Old age lives in a fluffy cloud.

Rebecca Duggins (9)
Race Leys Junior School, Bedworth

Anger

Anger is burning red
It smells like hot, burning toast
Anger tastes like sea water
It sounds like your heart pounding
It feels all hot and sweaty
Anger lives in a dustbin full of rubbish.

Katie Brown (10)
Race Leys Junior School, Bedworth

The 8th Of October - Cinquain

Hooray
It's my birthday
I rip the wrapping off
I see the gift, I say thank you
Next one?

Nathan Callaghan (11)
Race Leys Junior School, Bedworth

Christmas Thank You
(Based on 'Christmas Thank Yous' by Mick Gowar)

Dear Gran,
Thank you for the jumper
I love the colour blue
Even though it is big and sparkly blue
There's nothing scissors couldn't do.

Orlin Allton (11)
Race Leys Junior School, Bedworth

Seasons

There's no way to explain spring
There's no way to explain summer
There's no way to explain autumn
There's no way to explain winter
But most of all there's no way to explain
Why these seasons come each year.

Spring is flowery
Summer is sunny
Autumn is leafy
Winter is snowy
But why do these seasons come each year?

These seasons come
These seasons go
They stay with us
They disappear from us
But why do they come each year?

Rachael Richards (10)
Race Leys Junior School, Bedworth

A Dark Night

A dark night
A flash of light

A black cloud
A bang aloud

A bolt of light
A fearful sight

A catalogue to make me a
Thunderstorm!

Lauren Shepherd (10)
Race Leys Junior School, Bedworth

Winter

Winter is a fun season to have
Winter, we can play in the snow
Winter, children love
So come, come with us

Winter is good
Winter is bad
People are happy
People are sad
So watch out for your hats

Snow is fast
Snow is calm
Snow is heavy
Snow is no more

Snow you can hear
Snow you cannot
Snow is warm
Snow is not.

Chloe Crisp (8)
Race Leys Junior School, Bedworth

Super Duper Mum

My mum, she's a superstar,
I don't care if she ain't got a sports car!
She's cuddly and nice to me,
With her and my family we're as happy as can be!
She's my super duper mum!

My mum can be a bit strict sometimes,
But that's mainly my fault!
And really she treats everyone like a dime
And hides presents like a bolt!
She's my super duper mum!

Lucy Colley (9)
Race Leys Junior School, Bedworth

Christmas Thanks

(Based on 'Christmas Thank Yous' by Mick Gowar)

Dear Nan,
Oh what a pair of socks you bought,
They're really quite fantastic,
And I can't believe the pinky patterns,
They look so very gymnastic.

Dear Uncle,
Oh your lamp is very bright,
I've always wanted a light,
But please may I just say,
It's very annoying at night.

Dear Auntie,
Oh your hat was very comfy,
I didn't know that was what you bought,
With all the little fluffy bits,
It was a lovely thought.

Dear Grandad,
You don't need to feel bad,
I think you're very sane,
I spent that thirty quid you gave,
On a football, thanks again!

David Averre (10)
Race Leys Junior School, Bedworth

About Christmas - Cinquain

Christmas
Snow is falling
Christ is born at Christmas
One foot in snow and more to come
Santa.

Grace Brown (10)
Race Leys Junior School, Bedworth

A Christmas Thank You

(Based on 'Christmas Thank Yous' by Mick Gowar)

Dear Paul,
The flannel is terrific
So useful, such a lovely thought
I am bathing more
Thanks that you bought it.

Sian Flowers (11)
Race Leys Junior School, Bedworth

Cats

Some are skinny,
Some are fat,
Some sleep all day,
On a cosy mat.

Some are black
And some are white,
Some of them
Come out at night.

Some eat fish,
Some eat mice,
Some strange ones
Eat corn and rice.

Some of them climb trees,
Some of them climb walls
And very seldom ever fall.

Some of them have claws
Some of them have nails
Some of them run around all day
And climb up onto rails.

Madeleine Hall (9)
St Nicholas CE Middle School, Pinvin

A Pantomime

I've been in a pantomime
Called 'Jack and the Beanstalk'.
I enjoyed dancing and singing
One line did I talk.

Jack was a girl
And the dame was a man,
He made everyone laugh
As loud as they can.

Simple Simon was stupid
And wimpy too,
He had a cow
Called Daisy The Moo.

The giant needed a haircut
He had a helper called Grizz,
Who caught him a meal
And got in a terrible tizz.

His meal was Daisy
And Miranda for dessert,
Jack had to save them
And the giant he did hurt.

The finale was the best bit
Everybody clapped and cheered,
I hope I can do it again
Maybe next year?

Emily Bidwell (9)
St Nicholas CE Middle School, Pinvin

My Sisters Jess And Millie

My sister Millie can be as quiet as can be,
She puts a smile on her face when she sees me.

Sometimes she cries all the time,
It's very annoying and I say, 'Does she have to whine?'

Although on the other hand there is also Jessie,
Sometimes she can be oh so messy.

Although my sisters can be quite big pains,
I still love them even if they ruin my games.

Holly Slater (9)
St Nicholas CE Middle School, Pinvin

Waiting For Snow

It was the middle of January and I was waiting for snow,
I would look out of my window every morning hoping to see snow,
But the rooftops always looked bare and grey,
Not a single snowflake was to be seen.

That day I listened to the weatherman to hear
Whether there was any chance of snow,
He said there could be some,
But when I woke up the next morning, I realised that he was wrong.

I thought about what I could do if it snowed,
I could go tobogganing with friends or build a snowman,
I could have a snowball fight then come in for a
                                  hot chocolate by the fire,
I could have a day off school, perhaps even two!
My new wellies would finally be used.

But back at my window the rooftops look clear,
Still the snow stays away,
But whom can I blame?
Wait a moment, what's that on my windowpane?

Phillippa Cole (9)
St Nicholas CE Middle School, Pinvin

Goodnight

The fire is warm against my feet
I loved the fire and its heat
I put a blanket over my shoulder
And lent against a great big boulder
I looked out of the window at the rain
I thought it was a terrible shame
The thunder began to rumble
And logs on the fire began to crumble
I put my head down and went to sleep
The cat put his head up and had a peep
Goodnight everyone, it's time for a rest
I wish you all the very best.

Olivia Archer (10)
St Nicholas CE Middle School, Pinvin

Monster Poem

Monsters come in many sizes,
Most are found wearing disguises.

Big ones, little ones, scary ones,
Some have one eye, some have four
Hiding in caves or under the floor.

Pink ones, blue ones, many, many more
Hide in your room and shut your door.

Long arms, no arms, one head or two,
Are they coming to get you?

Do not worry, they aren't real
But what is that we can feel?

Jake Walker (9)
St Nicholas CE Middle School, Pinvin

Sauron Out Of Lord Of The Rings

His big red eyes like the blazing sun,
Searching for the ring of power this must be done.
He shall kill anything in his path,
He is searching through dirt and green, soft grass.

He stamps here and there with his bulky feet,
But the ring of power still he must seek.
His helmet disguises his face,
He is destroying this wondrous place.

Smashing houses, killing people,
Does he know the selfish Sméagol?
Living in Mordor with full deceit
Should he give the Uruk-hai their release?

The ring is getting closer to Mount Doom,
The evil spread will go soon.
Frodo holds it over the pit of fire,
Anyone who falls in will burn inside her.

He drops the ring and evil goes,
It could come back, who knows?

Hector Davies (11)
St Nicholas CE Middle School, Pinvin

The Flowers

Flowers can come in many different colours
And flowers can come in many different patterns.

Flowers are things that heal humans feelings
When they are dull and unhappy.

Flowers will make you feel happy
By smelling their lovely, sweet scent.

Flowers grow freely like a bird in the sky
Wishing that someday they'll never die.

Charlotte Harrington (10)
St Nicholas CE Middle School, Pinvin

The Monster Under My Bed

Well, I am Master Walker!
Logan is my name.
I live in a house at Inkberrow,
Number 5 Chestnut Lane.

I have a pet monster
Who I have named Jim.
He lives under my bed
But I'm not scared of him!

He comes out to play with me
When I go to bed at night,
But no one knows about him
As all day he's out of sight!

Jim plays with me on the PlayStation
Or we play hide-and-seek,
But when I've finished playing
Jim hides . . . and I go to sleep!

Logan Walker (9)
St Nicholas CE Middle School, Pinvin

Hamsters

H amsters are cute and cuddly
A nd they are smelly too.
M y hamster is soft and furry but why does she have to poo?
S ilver is my hamster's name
T o chew wallpaper is a game
E ating is her favourite thing.
R unning about is so much fun
    but surely not as much as eating a bun.

Eve Fraser (9)
St Nicholas CE Middle School, Pinvin

When A Dragon Came To Play With Me

I met a dragon the other day,
He wouldn't laugh and he wouldn't play,
I invited him round to my house,
But all he did was chase a mouse,
He didn't like the soup and bread,
But nearly bit my head off instead.
Mum was shocked at my dragon friend,
She thought she was going round the bend.
My mum said, 'Why don't you stay for tea?'
But the dragon simply stared at me.
I thought I'd take him to the park,
Mum said, 'Come back before it gets dark.'
Off we went down the road,
And round the corner we strode.
Guess what? What did we see?
A bigger dragon staring at me,
She looked so pleased to see her baby,
They might come back for tea, well, maybe.

Daniel Mead (9)
St Nicholas CE Middle School, Pinvin

What Cats Like To Do!

Cats are big,
Cats are small,
Some can be tiny,
Some can be tall,
They are so cute,
When they sleep in your boot,
But their favourite thing to do is play,
So leave them alone, don't worry,
They will find their way,
Put their food on a plate,
They will come, you just wait
And that is what a cat likes to do!

Paige Wyatt (10)
St Nicholas CE Middle School, Pinvin

The Hedgehog

He rolls like a ball all over the ground,
Picking up leaves without a sound,
As beautiful as it seems
Don't touch the spikes or you will . . .
Scream!

Jack Williams (9)
St Nicholas CE Middle School, Pinvin

The Seasons

I start this poem at day one,
The year has just begun,
At the moment I am cold and sharp,
The wind blows hard and chilly,
My touch makes the ground frosty,
I am winter.

Daffodils and tulips start to grow,
Cherry blossom appears on the trees,
The climate is getting warmer,
We look forward to the summer breeze,
I am spring.

The sun looks down and we are warm,
Paddling pools suddenly appear,
Barbecues are about,
Sea, sand and sun are fun,
I am summer.

Leaves start to fall,
The wind again starts to blow,
The nights start to draw in,
We light the fire,
I am autumn.

Alex Bradnick (10)
St Nicholas CE Middle School, Pinvin

It

A monster but somehow not,
Swims like a dolphin and slides like a snake
This being feeds on sea creatures
And lives in a cave nearby.
It likes the moonlight for some strange reason,
But is afraid of the sunlight.
It whispers words of terror,
And moves quickly, wanting to be invisible,
The great scales are there, for a secret never to be told.
When night falls the being blends with the walls of the cave!
We wonder why it does not harm the two-legged Earth dwellers
It waits until the tide is in and coast is clear,
Then unexpectedly, it slithers into the foaming, salty sea water
To hunt for the sea's best.
The cave is littered with leftovers of its prey
To the creature the sunlight is a threat!
The moonlight is its ally
The words of terror are spoken in a language that is unknown,
The talents of speed and invisibility are taught by the mind itself
The scales are made from sea pearls that glint in the darkness.
Each is a reminder of the sacrificed.
A creature such as this
Should not be found on this sand-perfect tropical bay
We wonder why and how it became the way it is,
Killing and destroying anything in its path
Inside the dreaded cave,
It lies alone waiting,
For hours, quietly,
Until it sights its prey!

'It' we call the being!

Megan Ramsay (10)
St Nicholas CE Middle School, Pinvin

My Big And Wild Family

I have a lovely mum,
I have a lovely dad,
I have a lovely sister, but sometimes she goes mad.
I have a dog called Tilly, she is a westie white,
She often is quite silly but she never seems to bite.
I have two super grandads
And a kindly gran and nan,
I have four lovely aunties, who are all my favourite fans.
I have four genius uncles, who are very good at magic,
They play some sports and laugh a lot, but sometimes are quite tragic.
This is all my family, we're big and wild and loud,
But there is one person who likes to smile
And that's me - Rebecca!

Rebecca Hutchings (10)
St Nicholas CE Middle School, Pinvin

Zindloo

'Monster, monster,
Where are you?'
'Scaring children in the night,
Giving them quite a fright,
When they're snuggled away in their duvet.'
'Monster, monster,
What do you look like?'
'Green and hairy and eight foot tall,
With the largest red eye of all,
With one large ear that spits out poisonous wax,
When something tries to attack.'
'Monster, monster,
Where do you live?'
'In a scrapyard under the rubble,
Eating my rhubarb crumble,
Mixed with children's blood and flesh.'

Kayleigh Juliff (9)
St Nicholas CE Middle School, Pinvin

All About Peter

I am a giraffe named Peter,
My legs measure about 3 metres.
All my friends make fun of me,
Because I'm tall and spotty.

I live in the bushy plains of Africa,
The home of the lion, rhino and zebra.
My neck is good for seeing over trees
And in my hair I can feel the breeze.

My thick, smooth skin is brown and yellow
And it is also as soft as a pillow.
My hooves are big, black and shiny
And my tongue is long, pink and slimy.

Louis Evans (11)
St Nicholas CE Middle School, Pinvin

Speed Boats

The ocean spray up in my face,
On the front of the boat with all the space.
The speed boat, skimming the sea,
All that ocean just for me,
Islands in the far distance,
Here and now there is no existence,
On this gleaming white boat,
Bobbing up and down I can tell it's afloat.
On this boat there is a warm, gentle breeze,
That makes me feel relaxed and at ease.
All my thoughts just drift away,
This is a beautiful day,
For riding a speedboat.

Rachel Corbett (10)
St Nicholas CE Middle School, Pinvin

The Beauty Of The World

Trees are swaying in the breeze,
The sun is setting over mighty seas.
As the evening turns into the night,
The beauty of the world is a wonderful sight.

Lights turn out now it's time for bed,
The night is silent - not a word to be said.
As the evening turns into the night,
The beauty of the world is a wonderful sight.

Stars are twinkling in the sky,
The wind blows out a long, deep sigh.
As the evening turns into the night,
The beauty of the world is a wonderful sight.

Now it's night the world is at rest,
Although she's asleep the Earth looks her best.
As the evening turns into the night,
The beauty of the world is a wonderful sight.

Lucy Hanson (11)
St Nicholas CE Middle School, Pinvin

Portugal

P lanning for my holiday is such fun.
O ff for two weeks in the sun.
R aining in England, lovely abroad,
T ravelling by plane, we're all aboard.
U p very early, to reach our villa,
G etting to the airport, the flight was a thriller.
A rriving in Faro, pick up the car,
L agoa our destination, it's not very far.

We get there at noon, not a moment too soon,
Jump in the pool, oh, it's so cool!
Later we drive to the beach,
The sea, sand and sun now in our reach.

Natalie Bray (11)
St Nicholas CE Middle School, Pinvin

Ferocious Lion

I jump further than my prey,
Swiftly swerving by,
Watch out or I will get you,
For I do not lie!

I am the ferocious lion,
See me dash,
Watch out or I will scratch you,
Slash, crash, bash!

Eyes watching like a spy,
Teeth as sharp as splintered wood,
Careful as you pass me by,
For I will eat you if I could!

Lucy Taylor (10)
St Nicholas CE Middle School, Pinvin

The Volcano

I can erupt at any time,
Everyone thinks that I was fine,
Until they get, closer to me,
I erupt in 1, 2, 3!

I can melt and kill people,
With my lava, that can ripple,
When I erupt, once or twice,
Everyone's scared, even the mice!

I can create, new islands,
I have made, the big highlands,
No other thing can do that,
Did you know, that is a fact!

Katie Hickinbotham (11)
St Nicholas CE Middle School, Pinvin

Space, Space

Space, space a wonderful thing,
Especially when you're wide on the wing.
Call for the ball when you're out wide,
And start a dangerous attack for your side.

When the ball comes, don't delay
Don't let the defenders stop you play.
Give your rivals a frightful scare
And show them a bit of that magical flair.

Get to the line to whip in a cross
Balls into the box will please the boss.
Hope your top scorer gets right up
A mighty header! We've won the cup.

The whistle blows, smiles all around
The stadium erupts with an incredible sound.
What a day! You've done your mum proud
As well as 50,000 fans in the crowd.

Space, space, a wonderful thing
Especially now you're the cup king.

Matthew Fellows (11)
St Nicholas CE Middle School, Pinvin

Snow Is Fun

Snow is fun, snow is great,
Everyone can hardly wait!
Some love it when others hate,
Snow comes early, snow comes late,
Can you believe it when it comes round here?
Snow also comes far and near,
Can you hear the children cheer?
Forget your troubles, don't have fear,
Run around and have some fun,
Right until the day is done!

Luke Ramsden (10)
St Nicholas CE Middle School, Pinvin

A Plane Flight

Swooping over the clouds, high in the sky,
Engine strong and loud, fields passing by.

Flying over water, a big ocean of blue,
Around it's getting wetter, windows covered in dew.

Flying back over land, the plane is starting to descend,
Ears are starting to pop, we all know it's the end.

Getting off the plane now, it's breezy off the plane,
Engine still going, getting back in lane.

Rosa Clubley (11)
St Nicholas CE Middle School, Pinvin

Hospital

Standing in reception
Ne-nor, ne-nor
Doctors getting paged
Bleep, bleep, bleep, bleep.

Paramedics in the staffroom
Chatter, chatter, chatter, chatter
Lots and lots of patients
Cough, cough, cough, cough.

Baby is in maternity
Wa wa wa wa
Ambulance coming through
Ne-nor, ne-nor.

Resus needed in the theatre
Help please, help please
Sleeping in the wards now
Zzz, zzz, zzz, zzz.

Chloe Faizey (11)
St Nicholas CE Middle School, Pinvin

My Sister

M y sister is very annoying, she drives me round the bend!
Y awning and groaning, I wish it would somehow end!

S ometimes it gets so bad we have a fight!
I always win and I prove I'm right!
S hhh! I tell her when we go to sleep!
T hen a car outside wakes her, beep, beep!
E very day we make up just sisters!
R eally we love each other but she always gets the whispers!

Ellie Cole (10)
St Nicholas CE Middle School, Pinvin

Stephanie Laura Bird

S is for smart, sensitive and silly,
T is for talkative, ticklish and talented,
E is for energetic, education and enthusiasm,
P is for popular, polite and positive,
H is for happy, heavenly and homely,
A is for adventurous, accurate and agreeable,
N is for natural, naughty and noisy,
I is for intelligent, imaginative and impatient,
E is for embarrassment, excitement and entertainment.

L is for loving, laughing and loud,
A is for animals, like antelopes and apes,
U is for untidy, unusual and useful,
R is for riding, responsible and reliable,
A is for ambition, activities and amusing.

B is for birds, boars and buffaloes,
I is for insects, inchworms and iguana,
R is for rabbits, raves and racehorses,
D is for dogs, ducks and doves.

Stephanie Bird (10)
St Nicholas CE Middle School, Pinvin

My Sister

My sister is so cruel,
She treats me like some fool.
She is always in a bad mood
And likes to scoff her food.

She takes so long in the shower,
Around about half an hour.
She always looks in the mirror
And her friend's mum is called Vera.

My sister is so terrible,
But I suppose she says I'm horrible.
And although this sounds quite mad
She really isn't that bad.

Siôn Roberts (9)
St Nicholas CE Middle School, Pinvin

School Photos

I really hate school photos
Pulling a funny grin
Sometimes I hate my pictures
Because I've got a double chin.

When Mum really likes the picture
I really do go mad
Seeing it up on the wall
Makes me feel bad.

When the photographer
Tells me to say cheese
I feel so embarrassed
I want to be stung by bees.

The next time we have school photos
I'm going to pull a horrid smile
That way Mum won't like it
And we won't have another for a while.

Abigail Jones (11)
St Nicholas CE Middle School, Pinvin

My Brother

M y brother is called Daniel and he's cool.
Y ou would love to watch him play football.

B y the way you could go and watch him if you want.
R ight you could say he is good at fighting as well.
O ur sister and brothership is not very good.
T he day goes on well until I get home then my mum and dad
    are shouting at my brother because he's being naughty.
H e and I are really like best friends.
E very sister and brother are like best friends really.
R eally good being with my sister and brother.

Jade Smith (10)
St Nicholas CE Middle School, Pinvin

Snow

A thin layer of snow
Falls every year or so,
In the time it's there
You can do anything you dare.

Sledging down the hill,
Requires a lot of skill,
Faster and faster, watch us go,
Until we start to slow.

Building a snowman is great,
He may even become your mate,
Dress him up in scarves and hats,
Make him slim or fat.

When the sun comes out,
We all shout,
For the snow will disappear,
We'll just have to wait till next year.

Anna Sime (10)
St Nicholas CE Middle School, Pinvin

A Vampire Teacher

Last night I saw my teacher,
A pale, thin, corpse-like bloke
Creeping round the churchyard
Wearing a pitch-black cloak.
He sat upon a gravestone
And he mumbled, 'Let me see,
To change into a bat
I have to say one, two, three.'
I saw a purple glimmer
And I heard a muffled bang
But just before he vanished
I caught a glimpse of a gleaming fang.
Next morning, in the classroom
Mr Meek, plump and pink,
Today I may buy garlic
And a crucifix I think!

Coral Gubbins (10)
St Nicholas CE Middle School, Pinvin

My Mum

My mum is warm,
From her heart,
To her touch.

I owe a lot of things
To people I know,
But to her so much.

I feel her arm turn
As she holds me
Day and night.

Without my mum
I would be no one,
No stars in my night or any sun.

Hannah Davis (9)
St Nicholas CE Middle School, Pinvin

The Matrix

The Matrix is unreal but cool
I don't understand why they disappear through a phone call
Trinity was the lady with the really dark hair
Falls in love with Neo and they make a lovely pair.
Morpheus was the boss of their little tribe
He walks around in black with greatest pride
Smith controls the Matrix and sits in an empty room
Waiting for the one
When Neo appeared in Smith's room the sun shone
Neo was the one.

Stephanie Weaver (10)
St Nicholas CE Middle School, Pinvin

The Hedgehog

Slowly creeping through the grass at night,
Although it's dark the moon's so bright.
Listening to the different sounds,
It hears a howl, of bloodhounds.

Crawling through the grass covered in morning dew
It stopped in silence, it finally knew,
That it was being watched.

A snowy owl in a tree,
Made him want to run and flee.
The owl watched his every move,
Running into the hedge to hide,
The owl flew down gliding side to side,
Quickly, quickly he must hide.

Dawn breaks, now he can rest,
Tucked up in his little nest.

Rosemary Hawthorn (10)
St Nicholas CE Middle School, Pinvin

My Favourite Animals

I like rabbits with fluffy tails,
I love dogs, they leave a trail
Of all the mud they dig up from the garden.

My hamster has a pink twitchy nose
And she has little tickly toes,
Which she uses to run around her tubes.

My old guinea pigs were really shy,
We only saw them when we put the dry
Sawdust in their cage.

Chinchillas are so adorable and fluffy,
No wonder they get so scruffy
When they go to bed.

All these animals are so sweet,
I can't think of anyone who would want to eat
The dog, the rabbit, the guinea pig, the hamster
Or the chinchilla.

Jessica Hawthorn (10)
St Nicholas CE Middle School, Pinvin

The Butterfly . . .

The butterfly flutters around,
In the jungle,
On the ground.

The butterfly flutters by,
Through the garden,
Why oh why?

The butterfly flutters away,
Over the hills
And far away over the bay.

Elizabeth Davis (11)
St Nicholas CE Middle School, Pinvin

Winter Walk

The glistening glass and frosted trees shimmered in the pale sunlight,
I gazed at the evergreens dosed in droplets of dew,
Cobwebs scattered in amongst the hedgerows,
Windows glistened in the sun
And snowdrops reared their heads amongst the dew,
These are the signs of winter.

Sam White-Edwards (11)
St Nicholas CE Middle School, Pinvin

Extract From 'It Was All A Dream'

I went to the doctors, to have my adenoids out,
But when Doc had a look, it turned out to be gout!
He said to me, 'Sonny, I'm sorry, you're going to die,'
And my mother, she embarrassed me, she started to cry!
'Oh Momma,' I said, 'it's no big deal,
You wouldn't be crying the way I feel.'
And what I said then was a comforting thing,
'Look at it this way, I've no more snuffling!'
Said my mum to me, 'Great, now I don't care you're gonna die,
'So let's go home, and I'll bake some yummy apple pie!'

As I was going home for my apple pie,
I started to wonder, *did I want to die?*
I started to think, *I'm too young to go,*
A coffin? A grave? Oh no, no, no!
I don't want to be crushed with a pile of earth,
I want to be with my friends, laughing with mirth.
Oh Joshua, oh Christian and even Ben,
I suppose I'll never see those guys again!
Oh dear, oh blimey, oh sacre bleu,
I wish things were how they once were!

Harry Mallinson (11)
St Nicholas CE Middle School, Pinvin

My Dog

My dog is always there
When she needs my care
She sits and waits for me
Until I get her tea.
She's by my feet all the way
She's getting older by the day.

My dog is lively and fun
But she weighs a ton.
She bounces not walks
And knows when someone talks.
Her tummy is quite fat
So she sleeps on her mat.

My dog is big and strong,
But is fairly long.
She eats from a bowl,
Then digs a big hole.
She runs with a stick,
Then greets you with a lick . . .

. . . I wish I had a pet
But I'm a full-time vet!

Lauren Ball (10)
St Nicholas CE Middle School, Pinvin

Teachers

T eachers are strict,
E ven in the well behaved lessons,
A lways grumpy and weird,
C hatting and easily annoyed,
H omework always set,
E asily excited,
R azor-sharp eyes to spot naughty children,
S houting all the time!

Lottie Woollaston (10)
St Nicholas CE Middle School, Pinvin

Do I Really Want To Know?

When I went into school one day,
I didn't know what the teacher would say,
When I walked through the classroom door,
All I heard was a great big snore,
Do I wake her - yes or no?
Do I really want to know,
What the teacher would say?

Would she say,
'Eat sweets all day?'
Would she say,
'Go out and play?'
Would she say 'Stay half the day?'
'OK,'
Do I really want to know,
What the teacher would say?

She might say 'Get out your books,'
She might give us dirty looks,
She might give us a yellow card,
She might make us work too hard,
She might make us pay attention,
She might put us in detention,
Do I really want to know
What the teacher would say?
I think I'll let her sleep all day,
Would you?

Kane Edwards (10)
St Nicholas CE Middle School, Pinvin

One Ring To Rule Them All

A ring,
Forged by Sauron,
Sauron's armies are strong,
Sauron's armies slaughter men.
He is powerful, bad, evil, dark,
Who is he?
Sauron, the Dark Lord of all time.

Frodo, the ring bearer,
A Hobbit, small, big feet and kind,
Had his finger bitten off,
The crime of this made by Gollum,
Who wants to steal the ring.

Nine companions set out with the ring
And destroyed it in the end.
Frodo, the ring bearer,
With Sam at his side.
Merry, Pippin - are two good friends
And they nearly died.
Aragorn a swordsman,
Legolas a bowman,
Gimli an axeman
And Boromir a swordsman.
Ninth and last, who slayed the Balrog?
Gandalf, the great wizard.

The first great battle between men, elves and orcs
Was won by our good side,
The rest of the great battles
Took place at two fortresses.
Great evil was shown, menacing and terrorising.
At last the ring was destroyed.

Alex Wagner (10)
St Nicholas CE Middle School, Pinvin

My Hobby

My name is Myles Weaver and painting is my hobby,
Not painting doors and window sills but war figures,
Painted with the disturbance of nobody.

Very carefully I paint each piece of armour and clothing
To the chosen colour of the army,
Good eyesight and attention to detail are the key,
Producing excellent workmanship I have my family loathing.

Silver, gold, black and red,
I cannot afford one mistake otherwise I get upset,
Left to dry, they look a treat standing in my bedroom,
Then off they go to my den in the loft to be rearranged and preset.

How chuffed I am to finish a box set,
Lucky my birthday is coming up soon,
I'd rather have figures to paint than have a pet,
Well maybe!

Myles Weaver (10)
St Nicholas CE Middle School, Pinvin

Puppy Word

I like all the attention I get,
But sometimes I wish I wasn't a pet.

In the day I go on my walks,
At night I watch this thing that talks.

I love it in the summer, it is so hot,
I get up to chase a cat but then I think not.

I look at the flowers in the park
And at night I look at the stars in the dark.

Before I go to sleep, I rustle about,
Then I organise my bed with my little snout.

Lucy Worthington (10)
St Nicholas CE Middle School, Pinvin

Winter

Look, look, look over there,
Look at that frozen icy pear.
Look at the snowflakes falling down,
Look at the snow all over the town.

Look, look, look over there,
Look at the children without a care,
Look at the snowballs flying around,
Look at them whizzing and hitting the ground.

Look, look, look over there,
Look at the hats on everyone's hair.
Look at the scarves around everyone's neck,
Look at the birds with nothing to peck.

Look, look, look over there,
Look at the snowman's happy stare,
Look at the wonderful Christmas tree,
Look at the smile that stays on me!

Felicity Parkinson-Allsopp (10)
St Nicholas CE Middle School, Pinvin

Sport

S port is fun
    It keeps you fit
    It makes you strong.

P laying lots of games
    Individually or as a team.

O ver hurdles, poles and obstacles
    With equipment or using your muscles.

R unning, jumping, throwing,
    Swimming, rowing, lifting.

T ime to cool down,
    Shower, relax, recover.

Felicity Hall (11)
St Nicholas CE Middle School, Pinvin

A Boat Ride Away

The waves soar high,
The wind shoots back,
The fishes dance
And dolphins jump,
The sun beats down,
All this is just a boat ride away.

There are life jackets, lifeguards,
Seatbelts and seat bars,
There are fishing nets,
And fishing rods,
Great whales to small fish,
All this is just a boat ride away.

Green, white, black, yellow,
And a sparkling shimmering blue,
Colours of an ocean or sea,
The breeze swishing in your face,
Or blowing you far back,
All this . . .

Is just a boat ride away.

Matthew Hancock (10)
St Nicholas CE Middle School, Pinvin

Football

F antastic game to watch,
O ver 90 minutes,
O rdinary people become stars,
T erraces to sit and stand,
B all flashing past the crowd,
A nxious managers waiting for success,
L inesmen and referee doing their best,
L osing is not an option.

Ellie Britton (11)
St Nicholas CE Middle School, Pinvin

My Family

My family, my family, my family are great,
My family, my family, my family are late,
My brother's are a pain, my mum is so vain,
But most of all my dog is very, very tame!
My hamster is called Sid, he climbs on his lid,
Our fish spend all day swimming around,
It looks like they're listening to every sound.
My brother's play football, sometimes in the hall,
I go to dance school, in lessons we have a strict rule,
That you can't act the fool!
My family, my family, I love them so,
My family, my family, we like to say hello.

Jodie Grant (10)
St Nicholas CE Middle School, Pinvin

My Guinea Pigs

My guinea pigs are very fat,
They like to eat, sit and chat.

They chat and squeak when I go by
And always look you in the eye.

My guinea pigs like to eat,
They also have very soft feet.

They have small backs and big fat bellies,
But even though they are quite smelly.

I've had them now for quite a while
And every day they make me smile.

Thomas Ward (10)
St Nicholas CE Middle School, Pinvin

Night

In the dark, my heart beats faster,
Unseen things lurk in corners,
In the night my fear is master,
Caught by my dreams I slumber.

Tossing and turning in my sleep,
Woken by the light of dawn,
That night I do not wish to keep,
As a new day begins.

Alexandra Gaynor (11)
St Nicholas CE Middle School, Pinvin

The Cat

Sun worshipper,
Night stalker,
Milk lapper,
Fur licker,
Mouse eater,
Fire lover,
Fish hooker,
Whisker twitcher,
Dog hater,
Silent padder,
Tree climber,
Back archer,
Bird watcher,
Claw spreader,
Quiet loner,
Shrill caller,
Purr generator,
The cat.

Bethany Powell (10)
St Nicholas CE Middle School, Pinvin

The Wildlife

I saw a fox prowling in the field,
With its beady eyes and its bushy tail,
As it was looking across the field it . . .
Saw a tasty treat.
'What can it be? What can it be?'

I saw a bird landing in the field,
With its flappy wings and its tiny eyes,
As it was looking into the grass it . . .
Saw a tasty treat.
'What can it be? What can it be?'

I saw a bee buzzing in the garden,
With its minute eyes and its tincy wings.
As it landed on a leaf it . . .
Saw a tasty treat.
'What can be it? What can it be?'

I saw a pheasant walking in the woods,
With its long tail and its coloured head,
As it searched through the mud it . . .
Saw a tasty treat.
'What can it be? What can it be?'

I saw a strange black thing in the garden,
'What can it be? What can it be?'
'I know . . . it's my puppy!'

Olivia Hartley (10)
St Nicholas CE Middle School, Pinvin

Spring

S heep giving birth to lambs in a field,
P retty flowers growing on the flower beds,
R owing boats out on the glittering water,
I rritating children wanting to go to the park,
N ewborn animals in sheds cuddling up to their mums,
G rowing children in the garden planting new flowers.

Rose Llewellyn (10)
St Nicholas CE Middle School, Pinvin

Hair Gel

H air gel is really cool, it's gooey and manky and colourful!
A aarrgghh! Is the sound of my mum when she sees my hair!
I cicles hang from my head as cold as a fridge.
R eally wet and horrible when I put it on my head!

G el is just simply the best thing on Earth,
E very gel is wicked but Garniér Paris is the best,
                                                better than all the rest.
L ove gel like it is a part of your family!

Ollie Tyler (10)
St Nicholas CE Middle School, Pinvin

Spring Is On Its Way!

Newborn lambs skipping in rings,
Stop to stare at tiny things,
They don't know what's wrong and right,
Cuddling under their mums at night.

Lovely spring flowers blooming,
Planting bulbs in autumn can be time consuming,
But all the work is worthwhile,
The pretty plants make me smile.

Birds busy building nests,
Flying around to get the best,
Getting their nests as comfy as can be,
Ready for their chicks to grow and flee.

The smell of freshly cut grass is sweet,
The grass is cut nice and neat,
We can't wait to go and play,
Spring is here, hip hip hooray.

Jessica Smith (11)
St Nicholas CE Middle School, Pinvin

I Wish It Was Saturday

I lie wide awake with my eyes tight shut,
Mum will be here soon with her 'time to get up',
If today was only Saturday, what fun it would be,
I'd run down the stairs and watch CBBC,
I'd get ready for football with a smile on my face.
To score in the game I'll call my friend Tom,
And shout down the phone, 'How'd you get on?'
He plays for the 9s, a year younger than me,
If someone asked me to play I'd be off like a flea,
I'd forget about my homework and other such stuff,
But here comes my mum with her 'time to get up'!

I wish it was Saturday.

Jack Parker (10)
St Nicholas CE Middle School, Pinvin

The Dolphin

I can jump as high as a cloud,
Play with my friends and
Be really loud.

I can swim really fast,
So I'll never be last.

I know my best trick,
So you better be quick.

I live everywhere,
And I don't even care!

I don't know my family very well,
There are lots so I can't tell.

My friends are good enough not to be true,
So they make a pretty good few.

I like my life very much,
So it is a good touch!

Sophie Tredwell (11)
St Nicholas CE Middle School, Pinvin

Animals

Pigs have pink, curly tails,
Snakes are really vicious and scary,
Cats are lively but lovely,
And monkeys are very hairy!

Chickens sit in nests and lay eggs,
Hamsters just run in their wheels,
Birds glide through the blue, clear skies,
Dodos are no longer real.

Spiders are creepy and horrid,
Mice are incredibly small,
Sheep eat grass and live in fields,
Fish swim around, that is all.

Lions are big and mean,
Cows are black and white,
Cheetahs are soft and spotty,
Bulls will put up a fight!

Some have four legs, others have two,
Many animals live in a zoo.

Diane Barker (10)
St Nicholas CE Middle School, Pinvin

My Phone

My phone is pink,
As pink as a rose,
I can flip it open and closed,
It's with me wherever I go,
I even take it in the snow,
I message my friends every day,
And play the games I play,
This is the phone I love so much,
That's why I can keep in touch!

Abbie Smith (10)
St Nicholas CE Middle School, Pinvin

The Mysterious Appearance

I lay my head for me to sleep,
A peaceful night without a peep,
When suddenly from in the gloom,
There came a shadow in my room,
I hid my head beneath my sheets,
My body shaking like a leaf,
I heard a howl,
I saw a shape,
The smell as bad as anyone could make,
What could I do? I dare not scream,
My mum and dad were nowhere to be seen,
The monster moved even closer,
Making slurping sounds which was even grosser,
I put out my hand to shield my face,
The monster licked me all over the place,
Oh what a relief, it's my faithful dog Spiffy,
I cannot believe he is so whiffy!

James Harley (9)
St Nicholas CE Middle School, Pinvin

Tiger

Tiger is old,
But Tiger is wise,
Thoughts of true wisdom,
Lie deep in his eyes.

The scars on his face,
Mark memories that last,
That he'd rather forget
And leave in the past.

But there are some memories,
He never forgets,
Like the hunters with guns
And the hunters with nets.

Fred Simmons (11)
St Nicholas CE Middle School, Pinvin

The Nightmare

Its eyes tell a truly shocking story,
Of fate, death and victory,
If you dare look into them,
You will be blinded for all eternity.

Its nose breathes out powerful flames,
From deep within its soul,
Its body spiky but slender,
With its scales as dark as coal.

Its teeth sharp as sorrow,
Longer and wider than me,
For tearing and ripping apart,
Flesh for breakfast, lunch and tea.

Its tail is for killing,
Its scared and lonely prey,
But some of them are lucky,
And live another day!

Its loathsome claws are like daggers,
Piercing into its meal,
Like sharks glistening teeth,
As it attacks its latest seal.

As it prowls back to its home,
A pitch-black, reeking cave,
It smells the smell of danger,
And starts to rant and rave.

As the sun begins to rise,
His creator starts to stir,
Its last and final moments,
Are beginning to occur
And the world as he knows it,
Slowly start to blur!

Ellie Pardoe (9)
St Nicholas CE Middle School, Pinvin

Ambitions

When I grow older I'd like a job,
Preferably on the stage,
Because I have some good ideas,
For a kid of my age.

Acting seems a good idea,
But knowing me it will take some years,
I will work hard and do my best,
And hopefully surpass the rest.

Football also sounds quite good,
Kicking the ball and hearing the thud,
It would be good to score a goal,
And then perform a victory roll.

Formula racing sounds good too,
If your car doesn't explode halfway through,
Spraying champagne sounds quite fun,
But if bees come along you'd better run.

I know that this sounds crazy,
But I'd like to be a spy,
Jumping out of planes,
And floating through the sky.

I'd like to be a soldier,
And go out on parade,
And get us out of trouble,
That we have made.

I would not be good as a doctor,
With reasons on hand,
Blood, guts and gore,
I just cannot stand.

I'd like to be a singer,
Goodness knows why,
All the notes I sing,
Are extremely high.

Danny James Sanders (10)
St Nicholas CE Middle School, Pinvin

My Mum, Dad And My Pet

My mum is super,
I don't know how she copes,
Rush here, rush there, that's all she does for us kids,
One day she'll give up and then we won't have a hope!

My dad is great on computers,
I don't know how he copes,
Find this software, find that software, that's all we ask him to do,
One day he'll give up then we won't have a hope!

My rabbit Peter is great at eating,
I don't know how he copes,
Want some carrot or broccoli?
That's all we give him to eat,
One day we won't have him as our compost bin
Then we won't have a hope!

Abi Pallett (10)
St Nicholas CE Middle School, Pinvin

In The Morning

Rise and shine, get out of that bed,
Prepare for your day, you sleepy head.

Pyjamas off, it's time to get dressed,
Trousers, shirt and don't forget the vest.

Choose your cereal, don't make a fuss,
Chop, chop or you'll miss the bus.

Pack your bag, what do you need?
Pencil case, folder, clarinet please.

Into the car now, seatbelt on,
But don't come back please,
At least not for long!

Hannah Fowler (11)
St Nicholas CE Middle School, Pinvin

My Star Of Remembrance

While my star twinkles in the moonlight,
My grandfather fights for England,
The star is taking care of him and God
And when the war was over, he is one of the
Survivors of the fight of England,
His gravestone for when he dies,
Will stand beside the other men in the army,
And his spirit will always be in the history
Of the Dowson family,
And my heart,
The poppies will always lie beside him,
And God is with him all the days he lies in his murky grave,
So when I see a poppy it reminds me of him,
And all the other men in the army.

Alex Dowson (9)
St Nicholas CE Middle School, Pinvin

Monster

There is a monster at school,
Who breaks every rule,
He's big, green and hairy,
I find him quite scary,
All the boys think he's terribly cool!

He steals people's lunches,
And eats all the Crunchies,
He hides people's coats away,
So at half past three,
When they're ready to flee,
He jumps out and eats
Them for tea!

Isobel Woolley (9)
St Nicholas CE Middle School, Pinvin

Monster Munch

I may be big and hairy
And I may be mean and tough
But I'm a nice, kind monster
And I've simply had enough!

It's really most enjoyable
When you cry and run away
I'm not going to eat you
We can play all day.

Oh, can't you see I'm lonely?
Can't you tell I'm feeling blue?
I've got no friends to talk to
But I like the look of you.

Don't let my dribble scare you
Don't be put off by my mouth
Take some time to get to know me
And we'll have a stunning laugh.

I'm just about to make some tea
I'm willing you to come
You will? Oh great, that's perfect
Ha, ha, I tricked you! Yum!

Cara Reed (9)
St Nicholas CE Middle School, Pinvin

Spaghetti

S lipping down your throat easily,
P asta in different shapes and forms,
   we like them however they come.
A nd with toppings they are, the nicest food in the world!
G eorge eats it three times a week,
H appily whenever it is served,
E lephants steal it whenever they can!
T eeth love to chomp on it,
T ummy rumbles when not fed spaghetti!
I love it!

George Crotty (9)
St Nicholas CE Middle School, Pinvin

The Magic Box

(Based on 'Magic Box' by Kit Wright)

I will put in the box . . .
A glittering piece from the sun,
A hoot from a gorgeous owl,
And a tusk from a trumpety elephant.

I will put in the box . . .
A sparkle from a star,
Silver spots from a leopard,
And a high-pitched noise from a dolphin.

I will put in the box . . .
A friendly lion's furry mane,
The rarest flower,
And a feather from the phoenix.

My box is fashioned from sparkling stars,
Blue glitter and gleaming diamonds.

On the lid is a phoenix with crimson and orange feathers,
In the corners are happiness and excitement
The hinges are made from a
Lavender unicorn's glimmering horn.

I shall fly gracefully in my box on a fantastic eagle
With golden feathers.

We shall fly everywhere together,
I shall sail the crystal blue seas on a
Rainbow sea horse.

Emily Cooper (9)
St Nicholas CE Middle School, Pinvin

Tanka - Snowflakes

Snowflakes tumbling down
Shattered crystals from the sky
Illuminating
Glittering without a sound
Twisting, turning whilst still cold.

Meg Chitty (10)
St Nicholas CE Middle School, Pinvin

The Dragon's Lair

The dragon's lair is far, far away,
In the land called Naja,
The deep, damp cave is as smelly as dog droppings,
No one dares to go to defeat him except for one man.

He goes up to the cave,
Where the dragon is sleeping,
He goes up the long winding stairs,
To meet the dragon.

He gets out his sword,
And runs up,
But *fire!*
No one saw him again.

Kinandeep Ojalae (10)
St Nicholas CE Middle School, Pinvin

Dinnertime

On your plate,
Your mom has hidden,
All those things
You have forbidden.
Sprouts, parsnips, carrots and swede,
Dad has grown them all from seed.
Thinking of pudding you have a dream,
Chocolate fudge cake covered in cream.
Treacle tart all over in custard,
You soon wake up covered in mustard,
In the air a voice you hear,
They will make you big and strong my dear!

Joanne Bull (10)
St Nicholas CE Middle School, Pinvin

One By One

One by one, one by one,
Children are dancing,
And having fun.

Two by two, two by two,
Ducks are quaking,
And cows say moo.

Three by three, three by three,
Adults and children,
Are out at sea.

Four by four, four by four,
Someone is knocking,
At my door.

Five by five, five by five,
The bees are buzzing
In their hive.

Six by six, six by six,
There's a hole in my wall,
That the builders can fix.

Seven by seven, seven by seven,
The angels are singing,
Way up in Heaven.

Eight by eight, eight by eight,
I'm having a party
So don't be late!

Nine by nine, nine by nine,
It's my birthday tomorrow,
All the presents are mine.

Ten by ten, ten by ten,
I can't write any more,
There's no ink in my pen.

Laura Madden (10)
St Nicholas CE Middle School, Pinvin

The Dolphin

I can swim as fast as an athlete,
Bah, bum, bah, bum goes my heartbeat,
I jump! I turn and dive through hoops,
Catching the fish in bounds and swoops.

I live in the ocean with many types of fish,
Some I play with and some as a dish,
I am oily and slippery, I stretch and I bend,
I'll always be there for you because
You're my friend.

Rhianon Hubbard (10)
St Nicholas CE Middle School, Pinvin

Monday To Saturday

Monday to Saturday I don't know what to do.
Monday to Saturday I don't have a clue.
I went into town and had a look around,
For ages and ages I looked and frowned.
Before I knew it in the corner of my eye
I saw a necklace holding a butterfly.
People just looked and thought it was cool,
It gave me good luck, 'cause we had a day off school!

Holly Adams (11)
St Nicholas CE Middle School, Pinvin

Life Is Special

L ove and respect the Earth you're on,
I nteresting things and boring things are just
  as good as other things.
F ind all new adventures in your life and make the most of it!
E ndangered animals must be kept for your children to see!

Richard Moynihan (9)
St Nicholas CE Middle School, Pinvin

Ben

I know of a dog whose name is Ben,
Who likes to walk, but he says when,
Where he goes he leads the way,
And Grampy follows come what may.

Ben is the boss though he's quite small,
He's as round in the body as he is tall,
He's black and white with a curly tail,
He's 17 years old and getting frail.

But even though he's getting older each day and
His black and white coat is turning grey,
He's a wonderful friend and fun to be with,
But doesn't like cats named Sam and Syd.

LucyAlice Harris (10)
St Nicholas CE Middle School, Pinvin

My Gerbils

A gerbil is my perfect pet,
A desert rat stays dry, not wet.
They dash around like little cars,
Up the tubes and round the bars.
Up and down the pipes they go,
Side to side, high and low.
They like to stand up on two feet,
Nibbling seeds and looking sweet.
They really love their plastic house,
It's fit for a gerbil, not a mouse.
When they're tired, they have a rest,
Sleeping in their sawdust nest.
I wonder how the gerbils feel,
Running round on their little wheel?
Maybe happy - maybe sad,
Maybe they're angry or possibly mad!

Huw Roberts (11)
Salford Priors Primary School, Salford Priors

My Cat Milly

My cat Milly is black and brown,
She's as brown as a witch's gown,
And she adventures all around town,
She has black eyes like a crooked hat,
And also likes to chase rats,
She's like my cat on the back of my broom,
She loves it when she's being groomed,
I love to see her when I'm sad,
She's by my side like my dad,
Milly likes to play with cotton wool,
But she does not like the swimming pool,
My cat Milly is like a sister,
And when I don't see her I really miss her,
I am proud of Milly, yes I am,
But if you want to play with her,
Catch her if you can!

Gemma Knight (11)
Salford Priors Primary School, Salford Priors

Guinea Pig, Guinea Pig

'Guinea pig, guinea pig, where have you been?'
'I've been in the garden eating my greens.'

'Guinea pig, guinea pig, what shall we do?'
'Nothing because I've caught the flu.'

'Guinea pig, guinea pig, shall I clean out your hutch?'
'No, not really, it's just too much.'

'Guinea pig, guinea pig,
Shall we have a chat?'
'Yes, but don't bring in the cat.'

'Guinea pig, guinea pig,
Shall we go to the vet?'
'No, I don't have enough mites yet!'

Jessica Robinson
Salford Priors Primary School, Salford Priors

Melted Chocolate

Melted chocolate in a pot,
I enjoy eating chocolate a lot,
It's smooth and creamy,
Which makes me dreamy,
Made from cocoa beans so weenie!

Melted chocolate in a pot,
Heated till it's boiling hot,
Its fumes are sweet,
Unlike my feet,
Which smell somewhat like rancid meat!

Melted chocolate in a pot,
I enjoy eating chocolate a lot,
Although it comes from sunny Spain,
And has suffered wet, wet English rain,
Sometimes it's the only thing that keeps me sane!

Melted chocolate in a pot,
Heated till it's boiling hot,
Lying there so dark and rich,
Bubbling like a cackling witch,
Hiding down a dark, dark ditch!

Melted chocolate in a pot,
I enjoy eating chocolate a lot,
Everyone runs to take their pick,
All that's left are spoons to lick,
Leaving me feeling so, so sick!

Jessica Pearson (10)
Salford Priors Primary School, Salford Priors

My Drag Bike

Waiting on the line, for the time,
For the Christmas tree to go green for me.
Open the throttle my head is down,
Knees are in, my heart is thumping with
An almighty pound.
Wheels spinning as the lights go green,
From the start line I cannot be seen,
The race is over, the times are flashing,
My dad says I did smashing?
It's a long way back to the pits,
I have to wait for my next fix,
Because I am a drag race,
Junkie!

Lilly Stedman
Salford Priors Primary School, Salford Priors

Teachers

Teachers here,
Teachers there,
Teachers are everywhere.

They wear smart clothes,
And go to bed in rich red robes,
They seem to know everything,
Like calculators just thinking and . . .
Bing, (they've got the answer)
They pull funny faces,
While you do your loose laces,
They seem suspicious,
And would like us to behave without fuss,
(Us? I don't think so).

Eleanor Jones (9)
Salford Priors Primary School, Salford Priors

Fish, Fish

I'm scaly and my scales look like sequins,

F ins in a variety of colours help us swim
And go through the green slimy seaweed,
I 'm a purple, blue and green fish and
Some of my friends are on a human's dish
But I'm the sort of fish that can't go on any dish.
S caly sequins green or blue which one suits you,
Green and blue are just fine but purple is more divine.
H ate dog fish, so do you,
See they love me and my cousin dolphin you may see.

Charlotte Pedreschi (10)
Salford Priors Primary School, Salford Priors

The Chocolates

White, milk and dark,
Some colour of snow, others coloured like tree bark,
The chocolates are for my dad,
Last year's birthday I forgot, yes he was mad,
Well I've seen him eating white,
Savouring it bite by bite.
Oh, I'll get something other,
What kind of clothes, oh bother!
I've bought the milk kind,
I'm sure they'll blow his mind.
'Here you are Dad,' I say,
'Let's see,' he says, he looks OK,
'Yum, I love these,
They've made me look easy to please!'

So Dad enjoyed his birthday
'Lucky' is what I say!

Emily Power (10)
Salford Priors Primary School, Salford Priors

Mother's Day

My mum is the best,
She's like a dozen pretty flowers in a peach vase.
Only butterflies and friends go to their home through a lonely heart,
This day is happy and dancing
Like a ballerina with the cheerful smiling sun.
Her life is active (trying to help), loving, caring and fun.
Edible food for my lunches for school are made especially by Mum.
Running isn't her thing,
Flowers are nice but sometimes glum.
I love my mum.
Sometimes I do a spring clean around the grumpy house.
Doing this so you can't see a single mouse.
Yes all the flowers in the field, tulips, daffodils, roses,
Are not as incredible as her but I'll gather them for posies!

Lucy Reynolds
Salford Priors Primary School, Salford Priors

View From The Window

We look out of the window, what do we see?
The birds bathing in puddles, flapping their wings.
The grass swaying in the breeze,
Of different colours of green,
Two cars parking in the drive,
One blue, one red,
Cars driving, going home for the night,
Already for their tea.
A bird rests for the spring, the tree swaying,
We look out of the window,
What do we see?

Joshua Payne (10)
Salford Priors Primary School, Salford Priors

Shopping

It was Saturday and the shops were busy,
The shopkeepers were in a tizzy.

I saw some pink knickers but who would wear them?
I could also see a frilly dress with a blue hem.

Buyers browsed for brilliant bargains,
I saw some note pads with wide margins.

I spied a pair of sterling silver hoops,
That had some twirly loops.

People were hot and dying for a coffee,
After that they popped into Thornton's for a tasteful toffee.

But by then it was time for more shopping,
The buses were constantly stopping.

A diamond was shining,
All around children were whining.

There were some fluffy socks that felt like a feather duster,
There were also some bobbles in a colourful cluster.

The sweet shops were busy, people waiting to be seated,
But the sugar dips were begging not to be eaten.

People hopped into cars on their way home,
They had a last stop for an ice cream cone.

The sun was dying down so slow,
The rowers were not going to row.

There was no sound of the tills, not even a ping,
The telephone had stopped not even a ring.

The shops were closed,
But the shops were not busy, it was the roads.

Emily Wright (9)
Salford Priors Primary School, Salford Priors

Different Things

An army jet goes as fast as sound,
A slug goes as slow as a snail,
An elephant is as fat as a house,
A snake is as thin as a stick,
A giraffe is as tall as a building,
A baby is as small as a mouse.

Things go fast, things so slow,
Things are fat, things are thin,
Things are tall, things are small.

Different things are good to have
Without them live would not be worth living.

Matthew Atkinson (9)
Salford Priors Primary School, Salford Priors

Coming Home From School

I was coming home from school
When I saw a big fat fool
I was sad
He was mad
On my way back from school.

The sky was as black as your hat
As I wiped my feet on the doormat
I was glad
He was bad
On my way back from school.

The dishes were piled sky high
The table began to cry
I was glum
He was dumb
On my way back from school.

John Smith (11)
Salford Priors Primary School, Salford Priors

Ice Cream

I love ice cream,
Ice cream all cold and yummy,
It makes my tummy feel all funny,
I could eat it any time of the day,
Though I wonder what my mum might say.
Strawberry, vanilla tastes so great,
Piled high upon my plate,
Chocolate has to be the best,
It really outshines all the rest,
If I hear a sound like a musical box,
It may be Mr Whippy coming round,
I'll grab my money and make my tummy
Feel all funny,
I love ice cream.

Laura Rowe (11)
Salford Priors Primary School, Salford Priors

The Cave

What lurks inside the gloomy cave
A creature from the dark,
Slowly he crept forwards
Then he heard a bark.

No one knows how he felt
When he heard this sound,
He flashed his light once or twice
And a creature is what he found.

No one knows until this day what it was he saw
The hiker was never seen again
In dead or living form,
But to find the beast that's insane
You will have to enter the depths of Stonecross Cave!

Robert Stainthorp (9)
The Willows CE Primary School, Stratford-upon-Avon

Bullies

B is for beat, hurt, abuse
U is for unacceptable, the behaviour of kids
L is for limbs, the ones that are broken
L is for lives, lives that are destroyed
I is for insults, words that are hurtful
E is for enemy - that's what you are to them
S is for spiteful - that's what some people are.

Hayley Ashton (10)
The Willows CE Primary School, Stratford-upon-Avon

Macbeth Poem

Obble, bobble, toil and trouble
Make this cauldron fill with trouble
Eye of a frog
Tail of a tiger
Fillet of a funny cat
Wool of a bat
String of a hat
A murdered man
Banquo's son
Rise spirit number one.

Obble, bobble, toil and trouble
Make this cauldron fill with trouble
Eye of a lion
Foot of a human
Ear of a worm
Leg of a kangaroo
Rise spirit number two.

Obble, bobble, toil and trouble
Make this cauldron fill with trouble
Eye of a crab
Skin of a giraffe
Leaf of a tree
Rise spirit number three.

Callum Marshall (8)
The Willows CE Primary School, Stratford-upon-Avon

Send A Cow

People in Asia
Are wearing away
Let's not just sit here
Do something today.

Give them some money
Or maybe a cow
When we give them one
They might say, 'Oh wow!'

Just have a quick go
It makes you feel good
To give them some seeds
To grow a small wood.

Save up your money
Give a pair of goats
Maybe when they're dead
They'll be good as coats.

Give some honey bees
Can sell the honey
In neat little jars
Get them some money.

And what about pigs?
I hear you might ask
Looking after them
Is a little task.

Maybe some chickens
To lay some nice eggs
And when they are frail
You can eat their legs.

Just give some money,
Just a little bit
Don't let them fall
Into the deep, dark pit.

Anna Jeffs (10)
The Willows CE Primary School, Stratford-upon-Avon

Getting On Stage

Nervous, scared, petrified
Really don't want to do it

It's too late to turn back now,
Crowd want me out there.
Really don't want to do it.

The curtains draw back
Time for my big break
Really must go out there
For my performance.

Crowd are roaring
Must go out,
Really don't want to do it.

Scared, very scared
Really don't want to do it

Abbie Howard (10)
The Willows CE Primary School, Stratford-upon-Avon

My Bedroom

Tatty old clothes all on the floor
A Barbie bed cover, 'Yuck!'
My brother's Action Man in the top drawer
I can't stand my room!
Pretty-coloured smelly socks
A Pizza Hut balloon
Chewing gum stuck on the floor
My dog's chewed my teddy bear
No curtains in the window
A big rotten tear
In my brand new trousers
Piles of homework to do
Fimbles pillow cases
My brother's old green goo
How much worse can it get?

Emily Arnold (10)
The Willows CE Primary School, Stratford-upon-Avon

Love Is Everything With A Family

My dad is a twit,
But I love him with a big bit
And that is my heart.

My mum is the best,
By far she is well dressed,
But I love her.

My sister is a pain,
I just can't explain,
But I love her so much.

I have come to the end,
Of who I think I love the most,
Oh I forgot somebody.

Me!
How could I forget me!
Now can you see.

Love is everything with a family!

Gregory Burge (10)
The Willows CE Primary School, Stratford-upon-Avon

What's Under My Bed?

What's under my bed?
Is there a monster?
Is there a ghost?
What could it be?
I'm scared! I'm frightened!
What if it comes out?
I don't like it.
I'm scared! I'm frightened!
It's shaking my bed.
I can hear voices . . .
It's coming closer
What can I do?

Amy Holt (10)
The Willows CE Primary School, Stratford-upon-Avon

I Didn't Do My Homework

I didn't do my homework because . . .
My pants were on fire.
My brother called me a liar.
My cat got fat.
I hit him with a bat.
The power went off.
Lots of moths flew away.
We went to the fair.
I met the mayor.

I didn't do my homework because . . .
We had a car crash.
For tea I had mash.
Sorry I didn't do my homework,
I'll do it I promise.

Zoe Walker (7)
The Willows CE Primary School, Stratford-upon-Avon

Under My Bed

Under my bed . . .
Old smelly socks from last year
Broken ruler from old pencil case
Big container with gone off beer
Cinderella book with ripped out pages
Squeaky toy my dog used to hear
Little teddy bear with one eye
3D shapes used to use in maths
My old toy bike that used to be fast
(And . . . something's . . . moving!)

Morgan Allen (9)
The Willows CE Primary School, Stratford-upon-Avon

Hamsters

Hamsters are cute
Hamsters are thoughtful
Hamsters carry food and more!
Hamsters are small
Hamsters are furry
Hamsters bite fingers and more!
Hamsters are kind
Hamsters are careful
Hamsters make good beds and more!
Hamsters are thin
Hamsters are cuddly
Hamsters have tails and more!

Alexander Harrington (10)
The Willows CE Primary School, Stratford-upon-Avon

In Bed At Night

One day at night I found myself in bed,
I heard some strange noises and this is what it said.
'Look under the bed, look under the bed,
Then you will know when you will be dead!'
I was lying down in such a fright,
I had to decide what was right.
So I looked under the bed,
My face was red,
But nothing was there.
I thought it was just a dream,
A very bad dream
So I just went to bed . . .

Christian Hall (10)
The Willows CE Primary School, Stratford-upon-Avon

Big Cats Or Little Cats!

We both have fur
We both have claws
We both have four legs
We both have paws!

We both have ears
We both have a nose
We both have a mouth
We both have toes!

We both have whiskers
We both have teeth
We both have tails
We both like beef!

But I'm big
And I'm small!

Deanna Jennings (10)
The Willows CE Primary School, Stratford-upon-Avon

In My Bedroom

In my bedroom
There's a great big rocking horse
One purple little clock
A dressing table
A cabinet
Lots of ornaments
A blow-up chair
A pile of clothes
Some teddies,
That's what's in my room.

Ellie Macleod (10)
The Willows CE Primary School, Stratford-upon-Avon

The Days Of Autumn

Golden brown leaves tumbling to the ground,
Stepping on leaves makes a crinkling sound.

Cars are frozen overnight,
They soon heat up though in the light.

Clouds are spiralling, blocking out the sun,
Letting out rain and making people run.

Harvesting, bringing in from the cold,
Rescuing sheep out from the fold.

Sun getting bleaker, warmer at home,
Comfy at home and outside alone.

At the month we should remember,
The 31st of November.

Autumn's over, winter's begun,
Much more cold and much less sun.

James Dyke (10)
The Willows CE Primary School, Stratford-upon-Avon

The Busy House

'T eatime - yippee!'
H e laughs.
'E at up your dinner while it's hot.'

B angers 'n' mash
'U must eat up all of it before your pudding,'
S ays Mum.
'Y ou're unfair.'

'H ow long is it until 'Corrie'?'
'O uch! I stubbed my toe.'
'U are silly!'
'S piders - I don't like them.'
'E at your dinner, stop messing about!'

Fiona Lewis (10)
The Willows CE Primary School, Stratford-upon-Avon

School Is A Nightmare

I hate school, it's so hated
I hate it, it is tainted
For all nursery kids beware
Because school is a nightmare.

Life at school, there is no rest
And think of that one little test
Good times when you were three
And don't forget the magic 'E'.

Life at school, school will kill you, see
And if you like the memories
Just remember the giant wrath
School will lead to the end of the path.

Spiros Beretoulis (10)
The Willows CE Primary School, Stratford-upon-Avon

In My Wardrobe

In my wardrobe . . .
The poshest of stuff
My wooden shoes from Holland
A scarf from London with fluff
My handbag from Toyland
And some chocolate from Cadbury World.
In my wardrobe . . .
The stupidest stuff
A Barbie doll with wings
And a dirty pair of pants
My old pink ballet shoes
And a creature kit with ants.

Paris Dealtry (10)
The Willows CE Primary School, Stratford-upon-Avon

Ssss!

Snakes are slithery, scaly and sneaky.
Snakes are long, large and never sleepy.
They're dangerous, daring, darting like spears.
They're reptiles winding around legs, nearing their prey.
Their venomous poison getting ready.
Jaws opening, it's getting nearer, nearer and nearer.
Sssss! Right on target!

Huda Mughal (10)
The Willows CE Primary School, Stratford-upon-Avon

A Macbeth Poem

Horrible, ugly, horrible hags
Wanting to eat you terribly mad
Wicked, ugly, horrible things
They're making bubbles with a bird's wing
What would you say
What would you do
If the horrible things tried to eat you?

Maisy Geddes (8)
The Willows CE Primary School, Stratford-upon-Avon

Ocean Blue

I'd love to see the ocean blue,
I'd love to see what I could do,
I'd love to see a whale or two,
I'd love to see you,
I'd love to see you on a dolphin riding up and down,
No matter what I do I want to see the ocean blue!

Hayfaa Bhatti (10)
The Willows CE Primary School, Stratford-upon-Avon

Macbeth Poem

Bubble bubble, terrible trouble.
Fire light things in the cauldron.
A fisherman's leg, a spider's silky web
Cauldron bubble, make some more trouble
A lizard's tail, a bat's wing, an eye of a rat
Fire burn, make some wild flowers
A crow's beak, a newt's leg.
Bubble bubble, make loads of trouble.
A beetle's arm, a horse's tail, a wool of sheep.
Bubble bubble, terrible trouble.
A pig's snout, a man's arm.
Bubble bubble, we three witches like to make trouble!

Jenner Finch (8)
The Willows CE Primary School, Stratford-upon-Avon

What's Under My Bed

It's screeching,
It's lurking,
It's making me scared,
I put my pillow over my face,
But nothing can stop it,
I pluck up my courage and look . . .
There's nothing, nothing at all.
I look away,
I hear it again,
My bed shakes,
What's going on?
I see a big shadow,
Help!

Siân-Annabelle Blinkhorne (9)
The Willows CE Primary School, Stratford-upon-Avon

Witches' Spell

W icked smiles upon their faces, frogs' tongues and lizard laces.
I cky eyeballs and a spider's web.
T iny bones of a mouse's leg.
C andy that tastes of dead rat.
H orrible guts from a cat.
E lephant ears all chopped in two.
S ewer water from down the loo.

Joanne Pearson (9)
The Willows CE Primary School, Stratford-upon-Avon

Topsi-Turvy Speed XIII

Igniting, illuminating, crackling like lightning
Whizzing, whirling, screeching like a banshee
Popping, prancing, spiralling like the wind
Sparkling, speeding, fading like an illusion.

Chavonne Brown (9)
The Willows CE Primary School, Stratford-upon-Avon

Farts

Farts are loud, farts are quiet, some can even start a riot
Farts are short and they're long, so how can they be wrong?
Some are OK, but some are fresh and smelly, that wrinkles up
your belly
Farts can last a long time, some just float away
But if your enemy's sitting next to you and does a big whopper
He's sure to have a bad day!

Cyrus Round (10)
The Willows CE Primary School, Stratford-upon-Avon

Go In The Cauldron

Go in the cauldron, my puppy dog tail,
Go in the cauldron, my feathers from a quail.
Don't go in the cauldron, my little black cat,
Oh no, it's gone in the pot - my hat!

Go in the cauldron, my jug of sick,
Go in the cauldron, my tub of toxic.
Put in my pack of germs
Stir it around, then add the wriggling worms.

Go in the cauldron, my legs from a frog,
Go in the cauldron, my fungus from a log.
Into the cauldron this all will go,
But I've made a mistake - oh no!

Go in the cauldron, part of my spell,
Go in the cauldron, water from the well.
Leave it to bubble and simmer away
And now I've got the spell to make a better day!

Kayleigh McFarlane (9)
The Willows CE Primary School, Stratford-upon-Avon

My Macbeth Poem

(Inspired by 'Macbeth')

Trouble, trouble, cauldron bubble
Foot of a lizard, toe of slug, claw of crab
And trouble, trouble, cauldron bubble
Skin of tiger, string of sheep, hand of human and mane of a lion
Trouble, trouble, cauldron bubble
A fish eye, a ghostly son, water from sewage
And trouble, trouble, cauldron bubble
Blood of a baby, head of a murderer and spirit of Banquo
Trouble, trouble, cauldron bubble, bang and splat that is *that!*

Rachael Finch (8)
The Willows CE Primary School, Stratford-upon-Avon

Kids Who Watch TV

Kids who watch cartoons
Are absolute buffoons.
They sit on the couch
Like a joey in its pouch.
This happens all over the world.
They watch TV
And don't pay their fee,
They sit there all day
Without going to pay
And Sundays they don't go to church.

Kane Hutchinson (9)
The Willows CE Primary School, Stratford-upon-Avon

The Dolphin

The dolphin leapt up from the sea,
It swam up to shore and up to me,
I stroked its smooth nose and it splashed water from the sea,
I had never met a dolphin that splashes water at me!

I got a beach ball from the beach,
Then I heard a seagull screech,
I saw a seagull on my friend,
Dolphin playtime never ends!

I threw the beach ball in the sea,
Then the seagull came and pecked at me,
The dolphin swam after the ball,
I faintly heard my mother call.

The dolphin hit the ball back,
I saw the seagull's wings flap,
Bye dolphin
Bye seagull!

Jessica O'Hara (11)
Witton Middle School, Droitwich

Leaves

In spring . . .
I was born
And began to yawn
I turned bright green
I saw things I had never seen
Life is new
I shine in the dew
I rise from my bed
A whole life ahead.

In summer . . .
I'm growing older
But never getting colder
I am soaking up the sun
Because life is fun
Providing shade
With a leafy glade
Thirsty for rain
I am feeling the pain.

In autumn . . .
I start to fall and turn brown and red
I start to fall into my bed
My life is over
My time is done
In spring my life had just begun
I am growing old and weak
Now I know the future's bleak
Now I begin to fall
While the trees are standing tall.

In winter . . .
Now I grow cold
I am too old
I will freeze and die
I do not know why
I get ready to begin a new life in spring
I wonder what the new life will bring.

Eleanor Gow (11)
Witton Middle School, Droitwich

Midnight

The golden face of the old grandfather clock,
Glowed in the darkness tick-tock,
Its hands were moving in a spooky kind of way,
Towards twelve o'clock the time ticking away.
The bats were all fluttering in the night sky,
The leaves were all rustling as they twirled by.
In the wind the spiky old trees, how they blew
As it howled in the darkness with a spooky kind of *oooh!*
As I gazed out my window on this cold, dark night,
A terrible sound gave me a fright,
But as I turned around and looked under the shelf,
It was only the grandfather clock all by itself.

Amelia Quiney (10)
Witton Middle School, Droitwich

Break Time

Hearing the bell, break time is here,
It makes us all smile, not even one tear.
We run around playing, making a noise,
The girls are as bad as the disobedient boys.
Hopscotch and skipping and all sorts of games,
The boys enjoy football and shouting out names.
Some play with yo-yos when the weather is fine,
But if it's raining we have wet playtime.
When the bell rings we stop all our play,
Back to our lessons and on with the day.

Ceri Ann Jones (9)
Witton Middle School, Droitwich

My Special Friend

My special friend
Isn't my best friend or my favourite.

My special friend
Is special because she's always there.

My special friend
Can keep a secret and be loyal.

My special friend
Always stands by me and never lets me down.

Alexander Peirce (11)
Witton Middle School, Droitwich

The Terrible Tsunami

Thousands and thousands of people died
While others lost their families . . .
The least we can do is sit back and watch TV
Starvation and thirst
Disease and sadness
All can be countered, if we give money . . .

Luke Pilot (11)
Witton Middle School, Droitwich

My Special Friend

He helped me when I was hurt,
He comforted me when I was scared,
He saved me when I was in danger,
He is my special friend.

Dale Hawkes (11)
Witton Middle School, Droitwich

Bright Blue Buttons

Tell me your problems
Tell me your pain
Tell me your worries
Tell me all your shame.
Try to be honest in what you say
This will help you at the end of the day.

I will try to help as much as I can
So don't be ashamed with the troubles on hand.
Don't keep them all cramped up inside
So let everyone know all your sorrow
Don't worry people won't tell you to shut up
In fact they'll probably cheer you up.

So in the end, at the end of the day
You will feel just like a little, bright blue button.

Harriet Hughes (11)
Witton Middle School, Droitwich

The Classroom Monster

It always creeps up on me, I'm sure it's got it in for me,
It goes to me and pulls me in
And after that it does much worse and throws me in the bin,
I've tried to tell the teacher, but she just laughs at me,
I'm sure I know what I see,
It gets me at the end of the day when everybody has left,
The worst of it is, it stares at me when I'm in a test,
It grabs me by its jaws and frightens me,
I seriously think that it has got it in for me,
I am warning you, do not go near,
For it nearly got me in tears.

Jemma Mortimer (10)
Witton Middle School, Droitwich

The Calm Monster

Its glimmering horses jump through the waves
Getting nearer to the golden sand.

It creeps forward tickling people's toes
Then suddenly rolls back.

Creeping forward, then rolling back,
Creeping forward, then rolling back.

The sun shines down on its turquoise face
Its soft, quiet voice saying, 'Shh,' to the people.

Creeping forward, then rolling back,
Creeping forward, then rolling back.

Anwen John (11)
Witton Middle School, Droitwich

That's My Hand!

This was the hand that used to play,
The hand that was always messy,
This was the hand that loved to paint,

This is the hand that writes this poem,
The hand that lends a hand,
This is the hand that strokes my dogs,

This is the hand that will steer the car,
The hand that will sign the cheque book,
This is the hand that will get wrinkly and old,
That's my hand!

Alice Spearing-Brown (10)
Witton Middle School, Droitwich

No One Knows That . . .

Harry Potter is by Lemony Snicket
Aston Villa is a team in cricket
Eight plus eight is thirty-six
A broken bone is impossible to fix.
Purple and orange go really well
Humpty Dumpty never fell
Einstein was really thick
Snail-pace is really quick.
Swimming costumes are very warm
It never rains in a storm
My baby sister's very old
Nothing is less precious than a brick of gold.
Cushions are very hard
No one ever gets a birthday card
Teachers' pets are really rebels
The largest stones are always pebbles.
Crocodiles make favourite pets
Fish are never caught with nets
Lip gloss goes on your toes
These are things that no one knows.
I wonder why I do?

Jess Goodall (10)
Witton Middle School, Droitwich

I Am . . .

(Based on 'Christmas Star' by John Rice)

I am the lorry that transports the trailer
I am the trailer that transports the box
I am the box that transports the car
I am the car that transports the battery
I am the battery that turns the wheels that turn on the car
I am the wheels that turn on the lorry
I am the lorry that trundles down the road.

Andrew Bishop (11)
Witton Middle School, Droitwich

My Magic Box

(Based on 'Magic Box' by Kit Wright)

I will put in my box . . .
A golden horse
Which will glint in the candlelight.

I will put in my box . . .
A tiny pebble and a wave from the deep blue sea.

I will put in my box . . .
A puppy with wet paws and a kitten with a fluffy tail.

I will put in my box . . .
A leaf off a tree and a tear from a child's eye.

My box shines and gleams with fairies living in the corners,
The hinges are made from threads of gold.

One day I will open my box
And let all of these things go.

Abbi Cottrell (9)
Witton Middle School, Droitwich

My Wedding Day

I was walking down the aisle,
everyone was looking at me,
with flowers in my hands,
and bridesmaids holding my dress.

Then my husband came,
wearing his suit and shiny shoes.
I had a tear in my eye as the ring was shown.
He gave me a kiss and held my hand,
everyone was cheering,
hopefully one day my dream will come true.

Elizabeth Hotham (11)
Witton Middle School, Droitwich

My Family

My mum always wants me to drink plain, old water
She says it's very good for her daughter

My dad is always on the run
But I don't know how he weighs a ton

I try not to argue with my brother
Even though he does act like my mother

I try not to push my sister down the stairs
Even if it's only to see if anyone cares

I try not to shake my cat
Even if he did kill a rat

My grandma is so lazy in the bath
But at night she likes to have a laugh

My grandad is so old
I think he's getting kind of bald

So this is what my family is like
Still they won't buy me that nice new bike.

Jasmine Davis (10)
Witton Middle School, Droitwich

My Life As A Pen

The zip has opened and light glows in,
She picks me up and takes off my lid.

I dream of the happy days when I sit there with my friends,
The zip unopened, but it's just a dream.

I hate the times she puts my head on the paper,
And slowly my energy is zero, I'm dead, I will never live.

And the day she twists my body
And gives me energy, I live again.

But then I fear the time I hear a crack,
Nooo, it's time for the bin, will I survive?

Gabrielle Smith (10)
Witton Middle School, Droitwich

Football Freak

I'm a football freak
My boots are sleek
My tackles are sharp
I play down the park
My kit is blue
The best team is Man U
The ball is red
I kick it over my head
My team is Lion
My captain is Ryan
I play midfield
Most of my bruises have healed
So this is it from the football freak
Whose tackles are sharp
And whose boots are sleek.

Jade Thompson (11)
Witton Middle School, Droitwich

Weird But Cool!

My 100 year old nan
is really weird
she sits at home
with her 4 foot beard.

She picks her nose
then puts it in the stew
she's not a good cook
that's all she can do.

But still she is really cool
even if she's 2 foot tall.

Matthew Ramage (10)
Witton Middle School, Droitwich

I Am The Pen

(Based on 'Christmas Star' by John Rice)

I am the pen
that sits by the board,

I am the board
that looks at the children,

I am the children
that play in the playground,

I am the playground
that sits in the sun,

I am the sun
that warms the flowers,

I am the flowers
that spray the seed,

I am the seeds
that grow a tree,

I am the tree
that makes the pen,

I am the pen
that sits by the board.

Kyley Hallett (11)
Witton Middle School, Droitwich

The Ice Monster

It froze me with its icy claws
and then it tried to kill me.

It froze me with its freezing feet
and then it tried to destroy me.

I fear its deep glare.
I dread its icy spiky hair.
I disgust its freezing stare.

Nathan Harold (11)
Witton Middle School, Droitwich

The Wardrobe Monster

It stared at me
with its evil eyes
and then it tried to control me.

It slapped me
with its wooden doors
and then it tried to catch me.

I live in fear of opening it
with its creepy dark back.

I think it knows I'm scared
it watches me through a crack.

I fear its greedy darkness
the way it seems to look.

To reach out when I'm sleeping
and hang me with a hook.

It stared at me
with its evil eyes
and then it tried to control me.

It slapped me
with its wooden doors
and then it tried to catch me.

Saskia Cossum (10)
Witton Middle School, Droitwich

Tsunami

T ough time for people hit
S tranded people cry for help
U nder houses people are trapped
N asty thing the tsunami was
A ny survivors grieve over their loss
M any die and few survive
 I n places sacrifices must be made.

William Brockett (10)
Witton Middle School, Droitwich

The Wardrobe Monster

It stared at me
with its evil eyes
and then it tried to control me.

It slapped me
with its wooden door
and then tried to catch me.

I live in fear of opening it
with its creepy dark eyes.

I think it knows I'm scared
for it watches me through a crack.

I fear its greedy looks
the way it seems to be in a mood.

To reach out for me
to be eaten by it for food.

It stared at me
with its wooden door
and then it tried to catch me.

Ashley Harris (10)
Witton Middle School, Droitwich

Tsunami Disaster

T errifying time when the tsunami hits
S creaming people running away
U ltimate disaster throughout the world
N asty thing a tsunami is
A nimals and food all washed up
M any towns got hit by it unexpectedly
I ncredible impact on the entire world.

Michael Kirkham (10)
Witton Middle School, Droitwich

The Classroom Chair

It grabbed me
with its long steel arms
and then it growled at me.

It bit me
with its plastic jaws
and then it squeezed me.

I live in fear of sitting
on its rough blue lap.

I sat down and it
threw me straight back off.

I hate its long, thin legs
the way they trip me up.

It catches me when I'm walking past
and I'm hurrying for a wee.

It grabbed me
with its long steel arms
and then it growled at me.

It bit me
with its plastic jaws
and then it squeezed me.

Lauren Whiteman (10)
Witton Middle School, Droitwich

Valentine's Day

Cards for everyone, for you and me
It's Valentine's Day just wait and see
Some with hearts on, some with flowers
Someone has sent one with magical powers
It's Valentine's Day for you and me
It's Valentine's Day just wait and see.

Cerise Bartlett (11)
Witton Middle School, Droitwich

Give Your Heart

(Inspired by the tsunami disaster - 26th December 2004)

With food in our bellies,
Clothes on our back,
With wide screen tellies
And a posh woven mat.
We have it all,
Wouldn't you say?
We have money which we spend day to day,
And spend it on things we don't need,
When people out there need a feed,
We need to help them,
They need looking after,
The girls, boys, women and men,
Donate something,
Clothes or cash,
Some of their houses might have gone smash,
So help them rebuild it,
Help them at least a little bit,
They won't have to suffer,
You'll stop their pain,
For them it'll be less tougher,
So they can start their life again,
Their loved ones might be dead,
So if you haven't got money,
Give your heart instead.

Alice Baren (9)
Witton Middle School, Droitwich

Friends

Secret giver,
Problem solver,
Fun helper,
Game player,
House visitor,
Phone caller,
Great chatter.

Charlotte Taylor (11)
Witton Middle School, Droitwich

What Would You Feel?

What would you feel if you lost your mum?
Then where would be the fun?

What would it be like if you lost your friends?
Then could you make amends?

What would happen if everyone gave up hope?
Then how could you cope?

What would you do if you were in the situation?
Even if you were dying from total starvation?

What would you just complain for more?
Or would you try to live, even though you were poor?

So please donate or just pray and kneel,
Because, what would you feel?

William Chambers (10)
Witton Middle School, Droitwich

No Safety Norman!

'Why shouldn't I drink this green liquid?'
'No Norman, no!'

'Why shouldn't I press this button?'
'No Norman, no!'

'Why shouldn't I pull this trigger?'
'No Norman, no!'

'Why shouldn't I yank this string?'
'No Norman, no!'

'Why shouldn't I walk this way?'
Whoops!
'Bye Norman, bye!'

Harry Bourne (10)
Witton Middle School, Droitwich

Teardrops

T eardrops come when you cry,
E vil things, give a tear to your eyes,
A re we really needing this sadness,
R ain reminds me of the crying loudness
D o we cry for no reason?
R idiculous, of course we do, at least once a season,
O uch! is heard when we hurt,
P eople can say something horrible, *now that really hurts*.

Beth Killing (11)
Witton Middle School, Droitwich

School

S chool is fun,
C hildren learn,
H ooray,
O ur school will continue,
O ur school will finish,
L earn more than you know!

Tyler-Rose Neath (10)
Witton Middle School, Droitwich

My Special Friend

Faith always makes me laugh,
She loves the same stuff I do.
When I'm feeling down,
She is always around.
She is the best,
I know she will always be there.
She supports me,
She always takes care of me.

Tamsyn Webley (11)
Witton Middle School, Droitwich

My Friend

My friend is my friend
She gets into strops
She can be a dare devil
Quite a lot of the time.

My friend has a great style
She likes to go for walks
She tries to rap
Which most of the time goes wrong.

My friend is great
Everything is cool about her
She's my best friend
She is the best person you could meet.

Naomi Collins (11)
Witton Middle School, Droitwich